TERESA ASHBY

◆

CORY'S GIRLS

Complete and Unabridged

LINFORD
Leicester

First published in Great Britain in 1993

First Linford Edition
published 2012

British Library CIP Data

Ashby, Teresa.
  Cory's girls. - - (Linford romance library)
  1. Love stories.
  2. Large type books.
  I. Title II. Series
  823.9'2–dc23

  ISBN 978–1–4448–1287–9

Published by
F. A. Thorpe (Publishing)
Anstey, Leicestershire

Set by Words & Graphics Ltd.
Anstey, Leicestershire
Printed and bound in Great Britain by
T. J. International Ltd., Padstow, Cornwall

This book is printed on acid-free paper

CORY'S GIRLS

Mark Jacobs returns to his home town to settle old scores, but learns that his ex-wife died two years before. Emma, his daughter from that marriage, and with whom he'd lost contact, is settled and happy with Cory Elliot, her stepfather, and her two half-sisters. But Mark wants her back, and when Cory has to go abroad on business, he leaves the girls with Katrina, who has to fight to keep the family together for Cory — the man she loves.

Books by Teresa Ashby
in the Linford Romance Library:

LOVE ON ICE
FOR THE CHILDREN'S SAKE
THE CALL OF HOME
A ONE-MAN WOMAN
FOOL'S PARADISE
CHERISH THE DREAM
WITHOUT A SHADOW OF DOUBT
TAKE A CHANCE ON ME
RUTH'S WAR

1

What am I doing here? The thought had gone through his head several times since he'd driven into the car park. Yet he could no more turn the car around and drive out than he could fly to the moon. He was here for a reason, a purpose and he knew he wouldn't rest easy until he'd done what he came to do.

The afternoon sun, reflected in the windows of the Anton Massey Building, glowed red behind a thin haze of cloud. Mark Jacobs remained sealed in his car, hands resting lightly on the steering wheel, his eyes as constant as the sun as he watched . . . and waited.

Things had changed in the town since he left ten years before. This building was new, standing where there had once been fields and trees. Then there was the new sprawl of the industrial estate to the west of the town, a giant housing estate to the east.

Suddenly, it seemed, someone had noticed the potential of the small town, realised that with its close proximity to London, it could be a useful site for development. That someone was Anton Massey, a rich man made richer by his foresight.

But Mark hadn't come back to look over his old home town. He'd come back to settle old scores, put a few things to rights. Yes, there were many, many things to be put right and it began here, at the Anton Massey Building.

It was just that it was taking a while for him to find the courage to walk in and ask for her by name. After all this time, she'd probably refuse to see him. Ten years with no contact apart from a monthly maintenance payment sent via the bank . . .

At least he'd been regular with that. There were times when he'd gone without in order to make the payment, but he never failed, not once.

Once he'd made up his mind to move, he was out of the car and striding toward the entrance of the building. He saw himself reflected in the brown, tinted glass and had to make a conscious effort to keep going. It was foolish to be so afraid, he told himself. She probably didn't even work here anymore!

When he asked for her by name, they'd probably look blank and say, 'Who?' And if he did see her, would she agreed to his request? It was a lot to ask after ten years, but since his life had taken shape, it had become important to him, almost an obsession.

By the time he was approaching the reception desk, his confidence was beginning to fail him.

'I wonder,' he said, smiling nervously, 'is it possible that Jo-ann Jacobs still works here?'

The girl behind the reception desk looked shocked and he rattled on, 'I mean, I'm not sure if she ever actually worked here, but I know she used to work for the Massey Corporation and — I'm probably clutching at straws, but — '

The girl had gone quite pale.

'I think you'd better speak to Miss Versey,' she said. 'She's our Personnel Manager. I'll just give her a buzz. Why don't you take a seat?'

'Surely you can tell me — '

'No, I'm afraid not.' She shook her head. 'Please sit down, I'll get Miss Versey right away.'

Within two minutes, the lift doors swished open and a young woman stepped out. She was younger than Mark, in her mid-twenties and had long, fair hair which she wore loose around her shoulders, caught back from her face with a black, velvet band.

As she approached him, her hand extended in greeting, he noticed her eyes, amber coloured, flecked with gold.

'Mr Jacobs.' She smiled. 'I'm Kirstina Versey.'

'Hello.' Her handshake was firm, he

noted, a sign of her confidence, yet her smile was nervous, wavering.

'You were asking about Jo-ann,' Kristina said. 'I think it would be best if you came up to my office. I'll put you in the picture.'

'What picture?' he asked, following her to the lift. 'Does Jo-ann work here or not? She used to be a secretary in the Personnel Department.'

The doors closed and he felt an uncomfortable prickling beginning at the base of his neck.

'Has something happened?' he pressed.

Kristina Versey refused to be drawn and said nothing. On the third floor, she led the way along a plushly carpeted corridor to an office which bore her name on a brass plate.

'Brass plate, eh?' Mark commented drily. 'You must be here to stay! Most places just use pieces of card slotted into the door!'

'Mr Massey treats his employees well. We don't have a very high turnover of staff,' Kristina said, closing the door firmly behind him and indicating a chair with a sweep of her hand. 'Please sit down, Mr Jacobs. Can I offer you a drink? Coffee? Something a little stronger perhaps?'

'Coffee,' he said. 'I tend to steer clear of the stronger stuff these days.' He smiled. He was proud of the fact that he could trust himself to run a pub without ever taking a drink. Jo-ann, he knew, would be surprised, perhaps even a little proud of him. His heavy drinking hadn't helped their marital problems, in fact it had probably worsened them.

Kristina got the coffee, then sat down on the other side of the large desk.

'About my ex-wife — ' he began. 'She did work here, didn't she? In the personnel department?'

'She was the manager before me,' Kristina said.

'Then where is she now?'

'I'm very sorry, Mr Jacobs,' she said. 'Jo-ann died two years ago.'

He stared at her for a moment,

hardly able to take it in. Jo-ann dead? But she was so alive, so vibrant, so young — two years ago, she'd have been just thirty-two. He couldn't believe it, couldn't imagine there not being a Jo-ann.

'I — I just can't,' his voice cracked. Of all the things he'd imagined . . . never this. Even after all this time, he found himself fighting against feelings he had thought long dead.

'It was a terrible shock for everyone,' Kristina said.

His forehead creased and he shook his head, still fighting disbelief.

'How? I mean, was she ill?'

That really was unthinkable. Jo-ann was the epitome of good health — at least she was when he was married to her.

'No, not really,' Kristina looked away. 'She was pregnant and there were complications. They managed to save the child, but there was nothing they could do for her. I'm so sorry, Mr Jacobs.'

'Pregnant?' He looked thoughtful.

'Then she had re-married?'

'Oh, yes.' Kristina's face softened. 'They were very happy. It was a tragedy that she died. I — I don't believe he's every really got over it.'

His mind was reeling. Jo-ann dead — how was it possible? But seeing Jo-ann was only part of his mission here, a very small part really.

'Where can I find him?' Mark asked softly.

'I don't think I can tell you that,' Kristina said, for the first time not meeting his steady gaze.

'Why not?'

'It wouldn't be . . . ethical.'

'Do you think it's particularly ethical that my ex-wife died two years ago and no-one bothered to let me know about it?' he demanded.

'I believe they tried to contact you through the bank, but — '

'It would have been difficult.' He shook his head. 'I've been working abroad for the best part of the last six years. In fact I only returned to this country a little over a year ago.'

'I'm sorry, Mr Jacobs, I really don't think I can help you.'

'Then tell me his name,' he pleaded.

She shook her head.

'I can't do that, Mr Jacobs. It's confidential information, but — I will speak to him and tell him that you were here — '

'Thank you.' He stood up. 'But whether he wants to see me or not, I'll find out. I will find out, Miss Versey, you can bank on that. There are a few things he and I have to settle.'

He closed his eyes. The news of Jo-ann's death changed everything. Now, he would have to completely re-think his plans.

★   ★   ★

'Hi, Dad, I'm home!' Emma came in through the kitchen and at once the house seemed full of her lively personality. Cory Elliot, standing at the breakfast bar, painstakingly cutting toast into thin soldiers, grinned at her.

'Good day at school?' he asked.

'All right.' She wrinkled her nose and banged her clarinet case down on the kitchen table.

'Hey, careful with that,' Cory cried.

'Sorry, Dad.' Emma grinned and two dimples appeared in her cheeks.

'Got any homework?'

'Maths. Can you help me later?'

'Sure,' he said. 'As long as it's nothing too difficult!'

'Come off it, Dad! You know you're a genius where maths — '

'Emma!'

There was a shriek from the next room then two pairs of eager feet pounded across the floor. Emma braced herself as her two sisters dashed into the kitchen, holding her arms ready to gather them both to her in a giant greeting hug.

Cory watched, feeling the familiar swelling of love and pride inside as he looked at his girls. There was Emma, so dark, so beautiful and the two little ones, their pale blonde hair and blue eyes a startling contrast to their sister. Jodie was four, Amy two and Emma had endless patience with them, far more than the little scamps deserved at times.

Most girls her age wouldn't be interested in their younger sisters, but the death of their mother had somehow bound the three of them together, even if the little ones didn't realise it.

'Tea's ready,' he said. 'Come on, girls. Eggs and soldiers!'

Emma picked Amy up and sat her down at the breakfast bar while Jodie scrambled on to a stool.

'I'll keep an eye on them, Dad, if you want to get some work done,' Emma said. She was already taking over, tying an apron over her school uniform.

'Thanks, sweetheart, I'd appreciate it.'

He hurried off to his study. He knew he was fortunate, being able to work from home, but it wasn't easy with two little girls under his feet all day. Emma was a great help, though, and he did most of his work when she was at home to take over.

Poor Emma. It seemed a lot of weight for her young shoulders, but it was a burden she seemed willing, even happy to bear. Perhaps taking care of her young sisters had helped her overcome her grief. At the time, she had seemed to be hit hardest by her mother's death.

For days, she had hardly spoken a word, hardly eaten a mouthful of food. She seemed to be lost in a permanent state of shock, then Cory brought Amy home from the hospital.

Seven days old and totally dependent, at first he'd been afraid that Emma would reject her baby sister, perhaps blaming her for their mother's death, but she hadn't. She'd taken Amy in her arms for the first time, had cried and Cory was flooded with relief.

Cleansed by her tears, Emma had fallen into the role of little mother, taking care of her young sisters whenever she was home. It was a role she shared with Cory and together, leaning on each other, drawing strength from dwindling reserves, they had forged a path through the darkest days of their despair.

Even so, a girl her age —

He heard laughter coming from the kitchen and smiled. Emma was all right, he decided, they all were. They'd survived a tragedy which could have torn them apart, but instead had pulled them together.

He looked at the photograph of Jo-ann which he kept on his desk and realised that now he could look at her face without it hurting. Of his girls, Jodie was most like her with her pale, blonde hair and vivid, blue eyes.

They'd had seven years together, seven happy years. There had been no suspicion, no indication at all that those years were to be cut so brutally short.

He even remembered their last conversation, held urgently over a telephone.

'The baby's coming,' she'd said, her voice a mixture of fear and joy. 'Emma's taken Jodie next door to Mrs Willis and Mr Willis is going to drive me to the hospital. Will you meet me there?'

'I'm on my way!' He'd already been on his feet, searching his pockets for his car keys. 'Sure you don't want me to pick you up and take you?'

'No, Mr Willis will be quicker and . . . and I don't think there's much time.'

'All right, darling,' he said. 'Take care, I'll be there as soon as I can.'

'Drive carefully . . . '

'I will. I love you, Jo-ann.'

'I love you, too.'

The line went dead. It was the last time she ever spoke to him for by the time he reached the hospital, she was already in a coma, hanging on to life by a fragile thread.

A light knock at his study door brought him back to the present.

'Dad.' It was Emma. 'They've eaten their tea. It's nice out, so I thought I'd take them to the playpark for a while, give you a bit of peace and quiet.'

'Sure, sweetheart, go ahead.'

She came into the office then, frowning.

'Dad,' she said, putting her arm around his shoulders, 'is something wrong?'

He covered her hand with his.

'I was just thinking about your mum,' he murmured.

'You loved her very much, didn't you?' Emma said.

'We all did.'

Emma nodded, then kissed the top of Cory's head.

'She'd be so proud of you, Dad . . . the way you've coped, the way you've managed to take care of the girls.'

'And you, she'd be proud of you, too,' he said, squeezing her hand. 'I wouldn't have been able to manage without you, but it's hard on you. You should be out, enjoying yourself with others your age, not stuck at home all the time taking care of two little children.'

'It's where I want to be, Dad,' she said so earnestly that he knew she was

15

speaking the truth. 'With you and the girls. Besides, I'd hate to think of Jodie and Amy going to a stranger! Anyway, I've the rest of my life to make up for anything I might be missing now. Not that I think I'm missing anything!' she added quickly.

'You're a good girl,' he said. 'I'll make it up to you one day, I promise.'

'Dad, you don't have to make anything up to me! Do you want me to repay you for looking after me?'

'Don't be daft!'

'Don't you be daft, then!' She laughed. 'I'll see you later. We should be about an hour.'

'Emma . . . ' he said. 'Be careful, love.'

2

'It's quiet here today!' Kristina noted as she stepped into the large, airy hall of the Elliot household. 'What have you done with them all?'

'Emma's taken them to the park,' Cory said, grinning. 'It was supposed to give me a chance to catch up on some work!'

'And I've disturbed you.' She pulled a face. 'A thousand apologies!'

'It's all right. I haven't been able to concentrate today anyway,' he said. 'Come through to the kitchen, I'll make some coffee.'

She watched him as he moved around the kitchen. He was tall, good looking with thick, light-brown hair and sad, grey eyes. When his wife died, he'd seemed broken, but somehow, he's put the pieces of his life back together.

'I've got a couple of floppy disks for

you,' she said. 'Mr Massey wanted you to see them before the data goes into the main computer.'

'Thanks, I'll take a look at them tonight.' He sat down on a stool and smiled across at her.

'I think,' she said, placing the disks on the bar, 'that they're quite — well, very important. Some European companies are interested in investing in Massey and Mr Massey wants them wooed. They're very keen, but it's going to take the personal touch to get them to sign on the dotted line!'

'Does Massey need foreign investment so badly?'

'I'm afraid so.' She sighed. 'The recession hit us as bad as it hit everyone else. It's a case of either attracting investment, or losing jobs. Two of our British backers pulled out on us today . . . and more could follow. That's why Mr Massey doesn't want that information made general knowledge just yet. If word gets out about this . . . well, I don't have to tell you how disastrous that could be for the company.'

'Right,' he said. 'I'll take a look later.'

Kristina was frowning. It was unusual for her and Cory reached across the bar and touched her arm. She jumped a little.

'What's up, Kristina? You haven't just called by to drop off a couple of disks have you?'

She shrugged. She'd been wondering how or even if she should tell him about Mark Jacobs. It seemed awful when he seemed to be at least getting over his wife's death to have something like this happen.

'Come on,' he urged. 'You can tell me! Maybe I can help.'

She looked at him, knowing that her feelings for him went far beyond straightforward friendship. If he ever found out . . . But she'd never let him find out because she didn't want to destroy their friendship. She doubted Cory was ready for another romance, sometimes doubted that he'd ever be. And even if he was, there was no reason on earth that he should choose her!

She was so different to Jo-ann. Jo-ann had been slim and willowy and very outgoing. She'd been popular with everyone.

Kristina was small and rather shy — at least where her social life was concerned. At work, though, she was every bit as capable and confident as Jo-ann had been.

'Kristina?'

'Oh!' She jolted back.

'What is it? What's wrong?'

'Cory, I — ' she began hesitantly.

'Come on.' He grinned. 'Spill the beans!'

'It's not me, Cory, it's you — '

'Me?'

'Mark Jacobs turned up at the office this afternoon. He didn't know about Jo-ann, he didn't even know that she'd re-married. I'm sorry to bring you this, Cory, but I thought you should know.'

Cory sat down and ran his hand across his face. She hated to see him looking so worried. He'd been through so much already.

'Is he bad news, Cory?' She couldn't be sure. Although she and Jo-ann had been friends, Jo-ann had never spoken of her former husband. It was almost as if she'd blocked out that part of her life.

'I don't know.' He looked at her. 'What does he want? Did he say? Why did he want to find Jo-ann again after so long?'

'He didn't say, but . . . he seemed eager to see you. He doesn't even know your name and I didn't tell him, but it shouldn't be too difficult for him to find out. I wanted to warn you, Cory.'

'Thanks, Kristina, you did the right thing. I guess I should see him, but . . . what do I say to him?' He looked at her, his grey eyes deeply troubled and she would have given anything to be able to help him.

'If it's any help, Cory, he seemed — ' She bit her lip. 'He seemed like a nice man. I don't think you've anything to fear from him.'

'You did the right thing, Kristina,

thank you,' Cory said. 'But if he gets in touch with you again, see if you can get him to leave an address or a phone number — somewhere I can contact him.'

'I should have done that anyway,' she said. 'I'm sorry, Cory, I didn't think. It took me rather by surprise, especially with him not knowing about Jo-ann.'

'No, that's OK.' He grinned. 'I wouldn't have thanked you if he'd turned up here out of the blue! It'll give me time to think things over. Now, drink your coffee and fill me in on all the office gossip!'

'Oh, so you've got several hours to spare, have you?'

'That good is it?'

'Oh, you know how it is at Massey. We've a couple of weddings in the offing and Mr Dunn from accounts is going to take early retirement.'

'All exciting stuff, then.' Cory laughed. 'What about you, Kristina? What are you getting up to these days?'

She shrugged her shoulders and

looked away. 'Not a lot,' she said.

'I don't believe that!' he exclaimed. 'A good-looking girl like you!'

She hid her sadness behind a dazzling smile. There was only one man she was interested in and he'd buried his heart along with his wife two years before.

★ ★ ★

The light was dying as Mark Jacobs entered the churchyard. Of all the places he'd expected to find Jo-ann . . .

He still couldn't believe she was dead, wouldn't believe it until he saw the evidence for himself. He didn't want to find out it was true. The big Norman church cast massive shadows, but he found the grave in the last patch of sunlight as it filtered through the twisted branches of a monkey-puzzle tree.

'Jo-ann . . . ' he whispered her name softly.

The stone was modest and as he read

the inscription, it was as though he were reading about a stranger, not the woman who had once been his wife. Their marriage had been short, passionate and their love too immature to stand the test of time, but he had loved her and he believed she'd loved him, once.

He crouched down and read.

JO-ANN VICTORIA ELLIOT
BELOVED WIFE OF CORY,
MOTHER OF EMMA,
JODIE AND AMY.
WE LOVE AND MISS YOU.

The name of the man he wanted to see was Cory Elliot. It was as simple, as easy, as that.

He stood up. Fresh flowers had been recently placed on the grave, which had been well tended.

Losing Jo-ann must have left a gaping hole in Cory Elliot's life. He hesitated, unsure of what to do next. Should he leave town and never come back, forget his reasons for coming here?

He looked again at the names on the stone and knew he couldn't leave. He'd come this far, if he left now without doing what he'd come to do, he'd never settle, never rest.

'I don't know who you are or where you are,' he whispered softly. 'But I'm going to find you, Cory Elliot because whether you realise it or not, something will have to be settled between us.'

★ ★ ★

The noise coming from the bathroom was deafening. Cory put his head around the door and saw his two youngest girls splashing each other in the bath, while Emma, covered in towels to protect her clothes, looked on, laughing.

'Calm down,' he said, feeling duty bound to assert some parental authority. 'There's water all over the floor.'

'I'll mop it up, Dad,' Emma said.

'They shouldn't be getting so excited

before bedtime,' he said.

'Can't you work?' Emma said and he realised she knew him better perhaps than he knew himself.

He shook his head. He hadn't mentioned anything to Emma about Mark Jacobs, saw no point in troubling her unnecessarily.

'How about you, have you done your homework?'

'Not yet,' she said. 'I'll do it once these two are in bed.'

'Let's get them settled now then,' he said. 'I'll dry Amy, you dry Jodie.'

For a while, as he helped Emma get the girls ready for bed, he forgot about Mark Jacobs and the threat he posed to their happiness.

Sitting quietly in a chair in the corner of the bedroom, he watched as Emma, sitting on a cane chair between the twin beds, told her sisters a story. When she'd finished, she kissed each of them good-night, then ushered Cory from the room.

'They'll soon be asleep,' she whispered.

'Right,' Cory said. 'You do your homework and I'll fix us some supper.'

'I can get us something,' Emma said quickly. 'Then you'll be able to get on with some work!'

'You've done enough!' Cory laughed. 'Homework, now! Do you want to eat in your room, or will you come downstairs?'

'I'll eat with you, Dad.' She smiled.

'Right,' he said. 'I'll call you when it's ready. Pizza all right?'

'Great! I'm starving. I wouldn't say no to some chips if there are any going!'

Downstairs, he put two pizzas in the oven and buttered some bread, his thoughts once again occupied with Mark Jacobs. He didn't even know what he looked like and Jo-ann had rarely spoken of him. The break up of their marriage and their subsequent divorce had all been quite amicable. Jo-ann had petitioned and Mark had never opposed it.

The doorbell disturbed his thoughts. He hurried to answer it, switching on the hall light and the courtesy light outside.

Opening the door, he came face to face with a tall, dark-haired man whose features were familiar. So familiar, that Cory found himself smiling in greeting.

'Cory Elliot?' the man said.

'Yes,' Cory said, only then realising that the warm, hazel eyes and the thick, dark hair, were similiar to Emma's.

'Mark Jacobs,' the stranger said.

'I've been half expecting you.' Cory nodded, his smile freezing on his lips. 'Come in.'

Mark stepped into the hall and looked around. He was tall, Cory noted, tall and strong with a pleasant face and so far at least, a pleasant manner. They shook hands and Cory noticed the man had a grip of iron.

'I've had a job finding you,' Mark said. 'I spoke to Kristina Versey, but she was reluctant to even give me your name for some reason. She seemed determined to protect your privacy.'

'I think you took her by surprise. I'm

sure she was acting as she thought best,' Cory said. 'She's not allowed to divulge information about any employee at Massey's without the employee's express permission. Come through.'

'She seems very loyal to you,' Mark commented.

'She's a close friend as well as a colleague,' Cory remarked.

Cory led the way into a large lounge and motioned to Mark to sit down.

'Can I get you a drink?'

'Not for me,' Mark said. 'I'll get straight to the point. I think that you know why I'm here.'

'Kristina told you about Jo-ann?' Cory said. 'I did try to contact you at the time, but your bank wasn't very helpful . . . and I'm afraid there was a lot to do, so letting you know what had happened wasn't a priority at the time. I'm sorry.'

'Yes, I'm sorry, too, but it couldn't be helped, anyway that's not why I'm here.' Mark paused.

'Jo-ann was a very special person,

29

you must miss her,' he said suddenly.

'All the time,' Cory confessed. 'How did you find me?'

'I visited the churchyard, found out your name from the stone, the rest was easy. All I had to do was look in the telephone directory.'

Cory sat down opposite Mark and the two men regarded each other for some time with mutual suspicion and a measure of hostility before Mark spoke again.

'There were fresh flowers on the grave — '

'Yes, we go regularly. I don't want the girls to ever forget their mother.'

'You have two daughters?'

'Three,' Cory corrected quickly and Mark laughed softly, almost mockingly.

'Three,' he raised his eyebrows.

'Jodie, Amy and . . . Emma,' Cory finished.

'They must miss Jo-ann,' Mark commented.

'Emma perhaps, but not the younger ones,' Cory said. 'Amy was less than an hour old when Jo-ann died and Jodie was only two. If Emma and I didn't keep Jo-ann's memory alive, then I doubt if even Jodie would remember her.' He stopped suddenly, frowning. 'Why wait so long before getting in touch, Mr Jacobs?'

'Mark, please,' Mark said. 'There's no point in us being formal. I'll be honest with you, Mr Elliot — '

'Cory.' Cory smiled thinly. 'As you say, there's no point in being formal. Let's try and keep this as friendly as possible.'

'Very well,' Mark said. 'After the split with Jo-ann, I drifted for a while, several years in fact — although I sent money regularly to Jo-ann,' he added.

'It's never been touched,' Cory said. 'Not a penny of it.'

'Well, it was there if she needed it.' Mark shrugged it off as though it no longer mattered. 'Then the chance to work abroad came up. It was regular and the money was good, so I took it. What should have been a two year contract stretched to five and, not to put too fine a point on it, I made quite a pile.'

'Good for you,' Cory said wrily.

'Although,' once again, Mark looked around, 'it seems that Jo-ann did pretty well for herself.'

'She worked hard,' Cory said. 'I met her when I joined Massey's.'

'Oh, you work there, too?'

'I work from home,' Cory said. 'You were telling me about your work abroad.'

'I came home some time ago and used the money I'd made to buy a pub. The Smugglers. It was run down, but I've been renovating it. The building's seventeenth century, all exposed beams, old ships timbers and big open fireplaces.'

'Sounds charming,' Cory remarked, wishing that Mark Jacobs would say what he had come to say and then leave.

'Oh, it is.' Mark smiled. 'It's a goldmine. I'm open all day and there's a thirty-seat restaurant which has been very popular.'

'You never remarried then?' Cory said.

'No, but I intend to. For the first time in my life, I feel really settled, Cory. I think, no, I know I can make a go of my business. The pub's in a nice village and there's a lot of land with it. Enough space for kids — '

Cory looked up sharply.

'And it's in easy reach of schools,' Mark went on quickly. 'I came here to see Jo-ann, talk to her, but when I learned of her death, I realised I'd have to change my plans drastically.'

'You sound as though you're trying to give me a reference about yourself! I think I know what you're trying to say, Mark,' Cory said. 'But you can't have thought it through. Ten years is a long time, a very long time — '

'I only know that blood's thicker than water!'

'That's not something I'd agree with — ' Cory said, breaking off when he heard footsteps on the stairs. Through the open lounge door, he saw Emma coming down and his heart began to thud wildly.

She came into the room looking every inch a teenage girl in tight, calf-length leggings topped with a huge baggy T-shirt. Her dark hair swung loose about her shoulders and she was clutching her school books.

She didn't notice Mark straight away.

'I've done my homework, but can you go through it with me, Dad? I'm not sure if I've done it right.'

'Sure, sweetheart,' Cory said. 'Emma, I — '

Mark was halfway to his feet.

'Will supper be long, I'm starving? And who was that at the door earlier?'

She came right into the room then and saw Mark Jacobs.

'Oh, sorry, I didn't realise you had company, Dad. Excuse me — ' She pulled a face and began to back out of the room.

Cory jumped to his feet.

'Emma, come back here, love.'

'Me?' She came back, eyed the

34

stranger suspiciously. She didn't like the way he was staring at her. His eyes seemed to be more inquiring than they had any right to be.

Cory put his arm around her. He was trembling, hoping she wouldn't be able to feel it.

'Emma, you know that your mother was married before,' Cory said gently, squeezing her shoulders tightly, and wishing desperately he could somehow shield her from all this.

'Of course,' she said.

Mark, impatient now and feeling that he'd already been messed around enough, stepped forward.

'Hello, Emma,' he said. 'I'm so glad to see you. I'm Mark Jacobs.'

She spun round, looked accusingly at Cory.

'Emma, love,' Cory said softly. 'This is your father.'

She turned once again to look at the stranger, the man she hadn't seen since she was a very small child. She certainly didn't remember him and when she looked back over her life, the only father she could ever remember having was Cory. Of course she knew he wasn't her real father, but she couldn't have loved him more if he had been.

Edging closer to Cory, she pressed against him, wanting him to hold her close and tell this man to go away. He put his arm around her in a protective gesture.

'Haven't you anything to say to me, Emma?' Mark asked. He sounded sad, his voice was thick with emotion.

She shook her head, unable to speak.

'I've come a long way to see you.'

'Perhaps you should leave now,' Cory suggested. 'It's been a shock for her. We'll arrange a time for you to come and see her.'

Mark glared coldly at Cory.

'Arrange a time to come and see her?' he repeated. 'She's my daughter! Are you suggesting I should make a formal arrangement in order to speak to her?'

'You've never attempted to see her

before!' Cory said, fighting to keep his voice level.

'It was Jo-ann's wish! She said it would be better for all of us if I just kept away. Do you think that was an easy decision for me to make?'

'It was entirely your choice,' Cory said softly. 'No-one could have forced you to make it.'

'No.' Mark smiled bitterly. 'No-one twisted my arm, but I was young, immature. It took a long time before I realised I'd made the wrong decision and by that time, it was too late.'

'So why come back now?' Cory said.

'Stop it!' Emma cried suddenly, tears springing to her eyes. 'Stop arguing about me, please!'

'I'm sorry, Emma,' Mark said. 'I never intended to upset you. Cory's right, we should arrange a proper meeting. We all need time to adjust, to come to terms with the situation.'

'That may be best.' Cory nodded. 'Under the circumstances . . .'

Mark turned to leave, but as he

passed Emma, he turned to look at her.

'Don't you remember me, Emma?' he asked desperately, his eyes pleading. 'I held you in my arms when you were just minutes old! I used to get up in the night to feed you, push you out in your pram. I was there when you took your first steps and the first word you ever said was 'Daddy'!'

'I don't know you!' Emma cried, clinging to Cory. 'Why have you come here? What do you want?'

Mark squared his shoulders.

'Now I'm settled, I wanted to see you again, Emma. It's been a long, long time I know, but I wouldn't have been any good for you before, I couldn't have offered you anything.

'Things have changed, I've changed. I came here intending to see you, but when I found out that Jo-ann had died, I realised that I'm all you've got. I want to take you home with me, Emma.'

'No!' Emma cried, horrified.

'I think you'd better leave,' Cory said. 'Can't you see she's upset?'

'All right,' Mark said. 'I'll go, but I'll be back. Emma's my daughter, she belongs with me.'

'Don't you think that's up to her?' Cory said, holding on tightly to the girl he'd always thought of as his own child.

'In the end, yes, it will be,' Mark said. 'But you've got to give her a chance to get to know me so that she can make her decision fairly. Legally, I doubt you have a leg to stand on. She's still Emma Jacobs, isn't she?'

'You know she is,' Cory said angrily. 'I tried to adopt her, but it was impossible without your consent and we were never able to contact you. What right do you have to come here after ten years? I doubt any fair judge would award you anything more than access rights!'

'Unless Emma decides that she wants to live with me,' Mark said confidently.

'After all this time?' Cory said. 'You're crazy.'

'We'll see,' Mark said. 'I'll leave you to think over what I've said, but I'll be in touch again. Goodbye, Emma. I'll see myself out.'

Cory held tightly to Emma until Mark had gone.

'I won't go with him,' she said fiercely. 'I won't leave you and Jodie and Amy, I won't! I'll run away first!'

'You won't have to, sweetheart,' Cory said, hugging her tightly. But in his heart he knew that Mark was right. And if he could make Emma change her mind, then there was nothing Cory could do to make her stay.

The thought of losing Emma re-opened the wound in his heart. And what of her sisters, Jodie and Amy? How would he ever explain this to them?

3

Kristina settled down in an armchair, curling her legs up beneath her and opening one of the files she'd brought home to work on. In the background the music of Bach played on her stereo.

Her hair was wound up on top of her head and she was comfortable in a sloppy track-suit.

When the telephone rang, the noise was so unexpected that she jumped.

'Krissy?' a cheerful voice said.

'Hello, Mum.' She smiled resignedly and closed the file on her lap.

'Why are you home? You should be out! I bet you're working, aren't you?'

'As a matter of fact — ' Kristina looked guiltily at the small stack of files on the coffee table, ' — I'm listening to music.'

'Oh! Are you alone?'

'Well . . . '

'Oh, my goodness!' Beatrice Versey cried. 'I am sorry, darling, I didn't mean to disturb you! Who is he? Someone gorgeous?'

'Well . . . '

'Look, you don't have to tell me about him now,' Beatrice Versey said, lowering her voice to a conspiratorial whisper. 'Give me a ring tomorrow evening and fill me in on all the details! You don't know how relieved I am that you're getting out and about at last. I know how conscientious you are with your work and everything, but a girl needs to get out and about!

'At your age, I was out every night, having fun — but don't tell your father that!' She laughed.

'Seriously, dear, I am glad. I mean, I'm not getting any younger and all my friends are grandmothers! Not that I want you to go having babies all over the place, but — '

It was Kristina's turn to laugh now. Her mother was a vivacious woman and rarely stopped talking, often talking herself into tight spots.

'You're digging a hole with your teeth, Mother!'

'You know what I mean, Krissy! I was thirty-eight when you were born — thirty-eight! If I'd known how much fun being a mother would be, I'd have started a good deal earlier. I just want a go at being a granny before I'm too old to enjoy that, too!'

'Got to go, Mother. I'll call you tomorrow. Take care — 'bye.'

She put the phone down and breathed a heavy sigh. Mothers! Thank goodness hers lived four hundred miles away — otherwise she'd be constantly parading suitable husband material under Kristina's nose!

She smiled to herself, wondering what her mother would make of it if she told her the truth? That the only man she was interested in was a widower with three children!

She laughed out loud and re-opened the file she was working on, hoping it would distract her from the problem of Cory Elliot.

★ ★ ★

It was quiet in the bar of The Smugglers. Paula Conway removed the cloths from the pumps and neatly folded them. She liked what Mark had done to this place. The newly-painted beams stood out black against the off-white-walls, which were hung with horse brasses on leather straps. The whole place had a wonderful atmosphere — old, but friendly and modern thinking. A family pub, Mark wanted and that's what he'd achieved.

It was the kind of place where people could bring their children and he never pushed drinks at anyone, preferring to make his money from the food side of the business. The place was steeped in history, too, built in the early sixteen hundreds as an inn.

There was a secret room in which smugglers had hidden themselves and their booty which was also used to hide Cavaliers, loyal to King Charles in a town which had been predominantly Parliamentarian.

Undoubtedly, The Smugglers had been at its most prosperous in the thirties, when the town had been an important port and its rooms had been let to the rich and famous. It lost something in the war years and by the fifties was just a rather run-down pub with sawdust on the floor and a few regulars to keep it from going completely broke.

Paula sighed, wondering what the dozens of previous landlords would think of it now!

'If only you could talk,' she spoke to the huge, open fireplace.

The telephone rang and she flushed, feeling silly for talking to a fireplace of all things!

'The Smugglers Inn,' she said.

'Paula, hi!'

'Mark.' Her face lit up. She was thirty years old with red hair, cut in a short bob, and pale-green eyes. She'd been a career girl, always maintaining that she'd never marry, never settle down — then she had met Mark and all that had been turned on its head.

'Any problems?' he said.

'No, except . . . I'm missing you!'

'I miss you, too,' he said, but it sounded more of a dutiful response than an honest, from-the-heart sentiment.

'Mark, when are you coming home?'

'Are you sure everything's all right?' he said. 'Sure you can cope?'

'Of course I'm sure! I just wish you'd tell me what was going on. And you didn't answer my question!'

She bit her lip. Ever since the renovations had been completed, Mark had seemed distant, absent even, as though his mind were now occupied by something else. Only he wouldn't tell her what it was. It frightened her. She'd never been in love before and didn't like the way it made her feel so vulnerable and afraid, yet it was too late to get out of it.

'I will,' he said.

'When? Look, Mark, I'm sorry, but all this secrecy is driving me mad! Where are you? What are you doing?'

The silence on the other end of the line seemed to go on for ever.

'Mark, are you still there?' she asked.

'We're going to have to talk,' he said at last. 'Something's come up, but it's not something I want to discuss over the phone.'

'Are you in some kind of trouble?'

'No.' He laughed. 'Is that what you think? No, there's no trouble, Paula, I promise you, just . . . Well, it's complicated. I'll come home and explain, then I may have to go away again for a while.'

She knew she'd have to be satisfied with that. Mark wasn't a man to be pushed and she'd just have to bide her time and wait for him.

'So when will you be home?'

'I've paid for the room for tonight, but I'll set off home first thing tomorrow. See if you can get John to do

47

the lunch time session, we can talk then.'

How typical of Mark not to want to waste the money already spent on his room! He was never ungenerous, but he was extremely careful with money. He'd never said, but Paula guessed there had been a time when he simply didn't have any that had taught him to respect what he did have.

'Mark . . . is it about us?'

'Partly,' he said. 'Don't worry,' his voice sounded warm again, concerned.

'I can't help worrying!'

'I love you.'

'I love you, too. Goodbye, Mark.'

She put the phone down and stared at the fireplace. What was it? What was he up to? She realised that she knew nothing about him, nothing at all! They'd met while she'd been nursing in Egypt and he'd never talked about his past, only his future.

He must have a past!

For the first time since she'd come back to England, she began to wish she'd never given up nursing. By moving into The Smugglers as landlady, she'd put all her eggs in one basket. Too much, too soon, she thought, for a man she didn't really know.

The door opened, customers came in and Paula smiled a dazzling smile of welcome.

'Good-morning,' she said, brightly.

★   ★   ★

Cory Elliot pulled into the vast car park of the Massey Building, his mind not on work, but on the events of the day before. Emma had been extremely quiet at breakfast, refusing to discuss the arrival of her father.

Cory blanched, still finding it hard to think of another man as Emma's dad! He'd never really given Mark Jacobs much thought and had certainly never seen him as posing any kind of a threat. Even before he'd married Jo-ann, he'd thought of Emma as his!

'Cory!' Kristina Versey came over to

his car. 'Why on earth are you sitting out here? Mr Massey's waiting for you.'

'Huh? Sorry.' He got out of the car, locked it and walked into the reception area with Kristina.

She looked at him curiously.

'Is everything all right, Cory?'

'No,' he murmured. 'Mark Jacobs turned up at my house last night. There was a bit of a scene, Emma got pretty upset . . . He's talking about taking her home with him!'

'But that's ridiculous!' Kristina said, pressing the lift button. 'He can't do that . . . can he?'

'I don't know.' Cory's shoulders slumped. 'I guess I should take legal advice, but once you involve law- yers — '

'You're afraid it'll get out of hand?' Kristina said.

The lift arrived, they got in.

'Wouldn't you be?' he asked. 'It could all blow up in my face!'

'I don't think you need worry,' Kristina said. 'Emma's lived with you for something like seven years and she's known you even longer than that! I can't see a fair judge — '

The lift jolted to a stop and they got out. Cory turned to look at her, appreciating her concern.

'He's her father,' he said. 'In name and in law. I don't have a leg to stand on.'

'Are you sure you're up to this meeting?' Kristina asked doubtfully. 'You look terrible! And it's very important.'

'Thanks, for that vote of confidence!' He grinned ruefully.

'Sorry.' She smiled. 'Come on, the big man's waiting for us!'

The big man, Anton Massey, was in actual fact a small man in his late sixties. Despite being plagued with ill-health, he was still the driving force behind Massey's success.

'You're late!' he said, peering over the top of half-rim spectacles.

'Sorry, sir, I . . . '

'That's all right, Cory!' He got to his

feet and held out his hand in greeting. 'I know how it is when you've young children to see to! How are your girls?'

'They're fine.' Cory smiled.

'That's good, good.' He sat back down and opened a file on his desk. 'You're managing to work from home still?'

Cory nodded.

'It's easier since we installed the computer,' he said. 'It's almost as good as being here.'

'Well, it's a good thing you young ones understand the computers because my knowledge is very basic! However, did those disks I sent you make any sense?'

'Yes, they did.' Cory smiled. 'I had a look at the data when the children were in bed. I agree that we should encourage these European investors — '

'Ah, yes, I knew you would.' Anton Massey smiled. 'And I believe that you're the very person to make it happen!'

'Me?'

'You always were a good ambassador for us,' Anton Massey said. 'You're a popular, likeable man and you know what you're talking about! How's your German and Dutch, Cory?'

'Rusty,' Cory admitted, grinning.

'Well, polish it! You're booked on a flight to Dusseldorf first thing tomorrow!'

'Dusseldorf! But . . . '

Anton Massey raised his hands.

'You've everything you need right here.' He passed a file across the table. 'Flight tickets, bookings, the lot! You're going on a tour of Europe, Cory, and I hope you'll return sometime next week with good news for the corporation!'

'I can't, sir . . . the girls!'

'Nonsense!' The older man laughed. 'If you can't find someone responsible to take care of them, I'll give Kristina the time off!'

Kristina's mouth dropped open.

'You'd like that, wouldn't you?' he barked at her.

'Well, yes, I would, but . . . sir, I think you're putting Cory in a rather unfair position, don't you?'

53

'Yes, I suppose I have rather thrust this upon you, Cory,' he agreed. 'All right, I'll give you until lunchtime to think about it.'

He stood up. Cory knew he was being dismissed.

'I'll call you at twelve,' he said.

'I'll be waiting. Just remember, Cory, the future of Massey hinges on getting that investment! I think you're the man to do it.'

Outside, Kristina said, 'Come to my office, I'll make you some coffee.'

'Thanks.' Cory smiled. 'Did you know anything about this?'

'Nothing definite,' she said. 'I knew he was planning to send you abroad, but I had no idea it was to be so soon. What are you going to do, Cory?'

He followed her into her office and sat down.

'Any other time, but now,' he sighed. 'How can I go away for a week with Mark Jacobs hanging about?'

She poured coffee and handed him a cup.

'You don't think he's likely to snatch Emma, or do anything silly, do you?' she said worriedly.

Cory laughed. 'No, I don't think so. He knows that doing something like that could jeopardise his chances. He's far too clever for such a stupid move.'

Kristina frowned, turning the problem over in her mind.

'Cory — ' she said, 'even if — I mean, if the worst happened and he did take Emma away, it wouldn't be the end of the world!'

'What?'

'Jo-ann was once married to him, he's Emma's father and she's such a nice girl. He can't be a bad person. All I'm saying is that — well, if she did go and live with him, that would be the very worst that could happen and . . . it isn't the end of the world, that's all.'

Cory looked at Kristina and felt sorry for the poor girl. She was doing her best to cheer him up and it must seem to her that she was failing miserably, possibly even making things worse.

I know what you're trying to say love,' he said. 'And you're right. If I look at the very worst that can happen, then whatever else happens, won't be so bad.'

'Sort of,' she said.

'It's just . . . I love her, Kristina. I couldn't love her more if she were as much my flesh and blood as Jodie and Amy.' He paled then. 'What would I tell them? They're only babies, they won't understand!'

'Cross that bridge when you come to it,' Kristina said. 'Right now, you've got to decide on this European trip.'

'I don't know what to do,' he said. 'I know I ought to go, but — '

'I think you should go,' she said firmly. 'Mr Massey's been very good to you, letting you work from home and everything! He's shown you a great deal of loyalty which you probably wouldn't have got anywhere else. I think the least you can do is show him the same kind of loyalty.'

'Loyalty,' he said. 'It all boils down to

that, doesn't it?'

'I'll stay at your house and look after the girls and I promise I won't let Emma leave home!'

He laughed. 'I'm sure it wouldn't come to that!'

'Then you've nothing to worry about. You go tomorrow, Cory, leave the girls to me. Trust me!'

'I do trust you, Kristina.' He smiled across at her, a smile which touched her heart. 'In fact, you're the only person I do trust.'

4

'How many shirts do you think you'll need, Dad?' Emma appeared in the bedroom doorway. 'There's enough for a clean one every day here. Do you want a spare? I can soon iron — '

'No, that's fine, sweetheart, really.' He smiled.

'Aren't you excited?' she said. 'I would be! All those places you'll be seeing!'

'I'm not going to have time for any sight-seeing.' He laughed. 'I'll try and send a postcard from every place I visit, though.'

He stopped packing and looked at her.

'I don't have to go. If you want me to stay here — '

'Oh, no, you don't get out of it that easily! Of course you must go! We'll be all right here with Kristina. Anyway, it's only for a week, I think we can manage to survive without you.'

He pushed rolled up socks down the side of his case and Emma huffed.

'Honestly, Dad! You're rumpling your shirts! Let me do it. You don't want to meet these important people looking as if you've slept in your clothes do you?'

'Emma, love, you don't have to do that.' He felt tears pricking at his eyes as he watched her busily rearranging his clothes. It wasn't right that a girl of her age should feel so responsible for a man who ought to be capable of looking after himself!

Perhaps she would be better off with Mark Jacobs! Perhaps with him, she'd be the child she should be and not forced into the role of a little housewife!

'I want to do it,' she said. 'I like taking care of you, Dad.'

He turned away, pretending to get something from his dressing table. When he turned around again, he'd regained his composure.

'Dad.' Emma straightened up. 'Do

you know why Mum divorced my
. . . Mark Jacobs?'

'Yes, love,' he said.

'Only you've never talked about him
and I don't think Mum ever did, either.
I'd never really thought about him
before, but now . . . Does it hurt you to
talk about him?'

'Me?' He sank down on the bed. 'Oh,
no, love. If there's something you need
to know, then ask and I'll try to tell
you.'

'Why did they split up?'

Cory closed his eyes. What would
Jo-ann's reply to this complicated
question have been? Would she have
gone back to the beginning, to their
wedding? Or would she have simply
answered Emma's questions? But how
could he answer that question without
going back to the beginning? He just
wished that Mark Jacobs had never
turned up to complicate their lives
— but he had.

'Sit down, Emma. It's a long story
and I only know part of it.'

She sat on a cane chair and crossed her legs, her face wearing such a sombre expression that it made Cory smile.

'Jo-ann and Mark met at college. He was something to do with the Student's Union and . . . they fell in love. She told me that she had never met anyone so exciting, so interesting!

'He played the drums for a band, had a good singing voice and was heavily involved in a drama group. He was a charismatic character, she said a lot of girls had a crush on him, but his head was in the clouds. They hadn't been going out together long when she found she was pregnant . . . with you, Emma,' he said, looking at his serious-faced stepdaughter.

'She was terrified about telling him, sure he wouldn't want to know, so she just dropped out of college with no explanations to anyone and went home. He wasn't as fickle as she thought and he followed her home, got the truth out of her and asked her to marry him.'

He broke off.

'Does it hurt you to talk about it?' Emma asked quietly.

'No,' he replied honestly. 'No, I never had any reason to doubt Jo-ann's love for me. When we met, her marriage had been over for a long time.'

'It sounds terribly romantic.' Emma's eyes sparkled. 'Go on, tell me what happened then?'

'Well, she married him. Neither of them came from particularly well-off families and he had to give up college to get a job. He did it willingly at the time, but ... Jo-ann said he never seemed to settle, flitting from one job to another.' He paused, choosing his next words carefully.

'You can't live on love, Emma, no matter how romantic that notion may sound and very soon they discovered that they had made a mistake. They were both young, desperate to do the right thing. They tried to make a go of it, but it proved impossible.

'Mark left, and they agreed that he

should make the break a completely clean one. Jo-ann didn't even want maintenance from him, but he sent money every month and Jo-ann had it put into an account in your name. The money's still there, Emma, it's never been touched.'

'But why did they split up?' Emma cried. 'People don't just fall out of love!'

'I'm afraid Jo-ann never talked about that. She liked talking about happy times in her life, but not the sad. I think, perhaps, that although they were in love, they didn't actually love each other. It's difficult to explain the difference, Emma.'

Emma frowned, her eyes darkening.

'Do you think it was something that my father did?'

'No.' Cory smiled. 'I don't think it's possible to apportion blame. It would be easier for you to understand perhaps, if I could tell you that he was unfaithful or cruel, but from what I know of him, he was none of those things.'

'Is he married? Does he have any other children?'

'I don't think so,' Cory said. 'I think he's going to get married soon.'

'He's quite handsome.' Emma smiled wistfully. 'I'd never really thought about him before. I wonder what he's like . . . I mean, I wonder if we have anything in common?'

'Probably.' Cory's heart ached. Emma was coming to terms with the situation, quicker than he expected and showing a lot of interest. It was only natural, he told himself, it didn't mean that he was going to lose her.

'Anyway,' he said, standing up and closing his case. 'It's getting late. You should be in bed.'

'Can we come and see you off at the airport tomorrow?'

'Sure! Kristina's coming first thing and I wanted to get her to run me to Heathrow. I'll write you a note for school.'

'Is there anything else you need, Dad?'

'Just a good-night kiss!'

Laughing, she kissed his forehead.

'I'll miss you, Emma,' he said.

'Oh, I bet!' She laughed. 'With all those glamorous air stewardesses to take care of you?'

'I'll be too busy!' he protested and laughed back.

Then the laughter stopped and he became serious again.

'You won't . . . make any decisions while I'm away?'

'About what?'

'Going to live with your . . . Mark Jacobs!'

'You're my dad!' She hugged him. 'It hadn't even entered my head about going to live with him! Don't you worry, Dad, I'll be here when you get home, I promise!'

★   ★   ★

'How's business?'

Paula jumped up from behind the bar.

'Oh, it's you!' she cried. 'You startled me! I wasn't expecting you for another hour at least.'

'Well, that's a fine greeting,' Mark teased. 'I thought you missed me? What were you doing on the floor?'

'I dropped my earring. I'll get John to take over, then we can talk.'

Paula, stupidly, felt herself blush, but that was the effect Mark had on her. In the short time she'd known him, he'd turned her whole life upside down, but as she made to walk away, he reached out and caught her hand, pulling her back towards him. His hazel eyes, flecked with gold, were almost smouldering.

'Don't look so worried.' He smiled gently. 'I love you! Nothing's happened to change that.'

'I'm glad to hear it.' She smiled nervously. 'I'll be back soon.'

She met him upstairs in the apartment. The ceilings were low, the windows tiny, but despite the darkness of the rooms, they were pleasant and welcoming.

He was sitting in a chair in front of

the open fire. Nervously, almost as though she were attending some kind of interview, she sat in the chair opposite his.

'Are you going to tell me what this is all about?' she said.

'You don't know anything about me, do you, Paula?'

She didn't answer. It was something to do with his past, she knew it!

'A long time ago, I was married. We were both young, we thought we were in love . . . Jo-ann was pregnant. The marriage didn't last, things didn't work out as we'd hoped and by the time our daughter was four years old, we were divorced.' He stopped, looking at her seriously.

'It was largely my fault. I went out drinking a lot, spent all our money in the pub and the more I did that, the more Jo-ann nagged and cried! The more she cried, the more I went out and got drunk. I was so immature and selfish!'

He closed his eyes for a moment.

Paula still said nothing. So far, it wasn't nearly as bad as she'd thought it would be.

'I must have put that girl through hell!' he said angrily. 'I grew to hate what I was and when we split up, it seemed the best thing for me to get right out of their lives. I'd already messed things up enough for everybody, so . . . I never saw either of them again.'

'That's very sad,' Paula said. 'A decision you regret now?'

'How did you know?'

'I think I know you better than either of us realised,' she said.

'For the first time, my life makes some sense,' he said, 'and that's largely thanks to you — no, it's entirely thanks to you.'

Smiling, he reached for her hand and held it in both his, stroking her skin and sending shivers down her spine.

'You, this place . . . I thought I could go to see Jo-ann and our daughter, re-establish contact. I've thought a lot

68

about Emma lately. She's fourteen
. . . a lovely girl.'

Paula started suddenly.

'You've seen her?'

'Oh, yes. Jo-ann's dead. She died two
years ago and Emma lives with her
stepfather, and his two daughters by my
ex-wife.' He shrugged his shoulders.

'Finding out about Jo-ann changed
everything,' he went on. 'I just wanted
to see Emma again, maybe have her
come to stay sometimes, but now I
know that Jo-ann's dead, I can't just
leave it at that.'

'I don't see why not,' Paula said,
frowning.

Don't you?' he asked in amazement.
'Emma is my daughter, my flesh and
blood and now her mother's dead, she
has no-one but me.'

'That's ridiculous,' Paula said. 'You
said she was living with her stepfather
and two sisters!'

'But he's not her real father,' Mark
said, jutting his jaw out stubbornly. 'I
can't leave her to be brought up by a

stranger! She belongs with me!'

'He won't be a stranger to her!' Paula cried. 'Only to you. Anyway, that's not the issue here.'

'Then what is?'

'Surely the question you should ask yourself is this, 'Is Emma happy' and if the answer is yes, then you have no right to go upsetting things.'

'It's not as black and white as that!'

'I think it is,' she said stubbornly. 'What about us? You and me . . . had you thought about that?'

'It makes no difference to us,' he said.

'But she's not my flesh and blood,' Paula remarked.

'That doesn't matter,' he snapped.

'Doesn't it? You seemed to place enormous importance on it a few moments ago. What's changed your mind?'

'You're twisting things!'

'No, Mark, I'm not.' She got up, walked to the window. She was trembling, clasping her hands together to stop them shaking. Eventually, she turned to look at him.

'You've got to think this through, give yourself more time, Mark. You're not thinking straight.'

'All right,' he sighed. 'But if I do bring her back here, to stay — '

'It makes no difference to my feelings for you, Mark,' she said softly. 'I love you. I can love your daughter, too. But I beg you, think carefully, Mark, think before you do anything.'

★　★　★

'Are you sure you don't mind driving me?' Cory said as he put his cases into the boot of Kristina's car.

'I don't mind,' she assured him. 'It'll be nice for the girls anyway.'

'You will drive carefully. The traffic around Heathrow — '

Kristina laughed. 'I know what it's like. I've probably been there more often than you have! And I will drive carefully, I promise. No harm will come

71

to your precious girls.'

He turned to see all three of them standing in a line watching him. Jodie and Amy with their big, blue eyes and Emma with her hazel eyes. They may only be half-sisters, he thought, but they all had that same look!

'They are precious.' He grinned. 'Worth more to me than all my gold!' He glanced at his watch. 'Right, shall we be off? I want to give us plenty of time to get to the airport.'

Kristina looked at Emma and pulled a face.

During the drive, they laughed and talked and Kristina thought how like a normal family they must appear, except that she was a little young to be Emma's mother. Thanks to Cory insisting they leave early, they arrived at Heathrow with an hour to spare.

'I'd rather you went straight home,' Cory told Kristina. 'There's no point hanging around just to wave to a plane.'

He crouched down and hugged his two little girls, then stood up and hugged Emma. Her hug lasted a little longer, Kristina noticed and she saw the anxiety in his eyes.

'She'll be fine,' she told him above Emma's head.

'I know.' He smiled weakly.

Even so, as Emma walked away with a sister holding tightly to each hand, the doubt remained in his eyes.

'I will take care of them,' Kristina said, touching his arm, a gesture of reassurance.

He turned to look at her then and he frowned, as though seeing her for the first time, really seeing her.

He raised his hand, touched her cheek then let his hand drop away.

'I know,' he said. 'Drive carefully, Kristina. Take care.'

She watched him go, then touched her cheek where his hand had been. The skin burned.

Amy fell asleep on the way home. Kristina was relieved as the little girl had started to grizzle.

'Do I have to go to school this afternoon?' Emma asked.

'Not if you don't want to.' Kristina laughed. 'Will you miss anything important?'

'C.D.T. that's all,' Emma said.

'Don't you like C.D.T.?'

'It's OK. I prefer games and maths.'

'Maths? My worst subject!' Kristina said.

'You won't be much help with the homework, then?'

'I doubt it!' Kristina admitted. 'Mind you, there's a program in the computer which you may find helpful.'

'Oh, oh!' Emma said. 'Jodie's asleep now! We're going to have trouble getting those two to go to sleep tonight!'

'We'll just have to make sure they're tired out by bedtime, then!' Kristina laughed. 'Let's go to the pool this afternoon, get some exercise!'

'Great!' Emma said.

She's just a little girl, Kristina thought. For all her grown-up ways and her common sense, deep down, she's just a child.

'Don't you want to get married, Kristina?'

'One day, maybe,' Kristina said, unruffled by the suddeness of Emma's frank question. 'How about you?'

'I don't know — never really thought. I suppose if I met someone like Dad . . . Cory, that is.'

Kristina glanced at Emma and saw she was frowning. She was confused, to suddenly find herself with two dads.

'Why don't you call Cory your dad and Mark your father?' Kristina suggested. 'That way I'll know who you're talking about!'

'You don't mind me talking about my father then?'

'Why should I?'

Emma shrugged.

'Look, Emma, he's your father. Cory won't stop you seeing him if that's what you want.'

Emma fell silent for the rest of the journey home, deep in thought. Kristina was relieved when they reached home, but the relief was short-lived when she saw an unfamiliar car parked outside.

She pulled up on the drive and in her rear view mirror, she saw the other driver getting out of the other car and following them.

It was Mark Jacobs.

As if on cue, as soon as the car stopped, Jodie and Amy both started to cry. Emma got out of the car and faced her father down the length of the drive.

Kristina watched as Mark Jacobs raised his hand in greeting. Emma waved back.

'It's all right, girls.' Kristina ducked into the back of the car to comfort the two little ones. 'We're home now! Let's go inside and have a nice drink.'

She calmed them down and by the time she'd unstrapped them from their safety seats and stood them on the drive. Emma was talking to her father.

'Emma!' Kristina called.

'It's all right if my father comes in for a cup of coffee, isn't it, Kristina?' Emma said hesitantly.

'Well, I — ' Kristina felt her heart beginning to pound. She felt she ought to say no, but how could she refuse when this was Emma's home and this man was Emma's father?'

'I don't see that it will do any harm,' Kristina said at last. Emma was like her mother, friendly, outgoing and she was aready chatting to her father as thought they were old friends.

Kristina, carrying Amy and holding Jodie's hand, followed Emma and Mark into the house.

She felt as though she were being terribly disloyal to Cory, letting Mark Jacobs into his house the minute he'd gone away on business. It was almost as if the whole thing had been planned.

'Who's that man?' Jodie tugged at Kristina's hand.

Looking down into those big, blue eyes, Kristina didn't know what to say. How could she tell the child that it was Emma's father?

'He's . . . he's a friend of daddy's,' she said at last, then Emma laughed out loud ahead of them and Kristina's feelings of unease increased.

5

Two days and it felt more like two weeks — how did he cope? Kristina felt worn out, but happily so. It was a different kind of tired to what she normally felt after a busy day at the office.

She'd often thought how she'd like a big family of her own, but the trouble with that ambition was, she'd need a man to share it with and so far, she just hadn't met anyone she'd care to spend the rest of her life with.

Except Cory.

And Cory was very much in love with the memory of his wife. There were pictures of her in almost every room in the house, But Kristina didn't need photographs to jog her memory so far as Jo-ann was concerned. It had been Jo-ann who had interviewed her for her job at Massey.

She'd been terrified, but Jo-ann had been kind and sympathetic and had quickly put Kristina at her ease.

'You never know,' Jo-ann had said, with what it turned out to be a degree of prophecy. 'You may end up sitting in this chair one day!'

And she had. When Jo-ann left work to have Jodie, Kristina stepped into her shoes. She remembered Jo-ann coming into the office when Jodie was just a toddler.

'Guess what!' she'd said, tearfully. 'I'm pregnant again! Just when I thought the end was in sight!'

'End of what?' Kristina had asked, puzzled.

'All this.' She had lifted a bag of disposable nappies up in the air. 'Another two or three years and I would have been able to come back to work — now . . . Oh, I just feel so . . . so hard done by!'

Then she had burst out laughing and Kristina joined in.

'Don't take any notice of me,

Kristina,' Jo-ann had said. 'It's my hormones! I'll be fine once they settle down!'

Sighing, Kristina began to feed washing into the machine. It was incredible how many clothes the girls had got through in two days! At least the two little ones were in bed and asleep now and Emma was out. She looked at the electric clock on the wall and bit her lip. She should have been home by now.

The phone rang and she hurried to answer it.

'Kristina? Hi, it's me, Cory.'

'Hello, Cory,' she said.

'I haven't disturbed you, have I?' he asked, a tinge of concern coming to his voice. 'You weren't watching something on television, were you?'

'Chance would be a fine thing.' She laughed. 'I haven't seen any TV at all — unless you count cartoons and Thomas the Tank Engine!'

'Sounds ominous! I take it they're keeping you busy.'

'Not really. I was just loading up the washing machine. Where are you now?'

'Paris.' He sounded fed up. 'I'm going on to Rome in the morning.'

'Is it going well, do you think?'

'So far, yes, very well. I think the tea lady could have got them to sign up for us! Anton underestimated their interest.'

'So, what's the weather like in Paris?'

'Raining,' he said. 'It's been raining cats and dogs everywhere — I must be travelling beneath my very own black cloud. How's it been at home?'

'Dry, sunny — exactly as you'd expect!'

'So,' he said. 'You've no problems? Nothing you can't handle? Jodie and Amy in bed?'

'Fast asleep. I've found the trick is to keep them really busy all day and they crash out totally around seven o'clock and don't surface for a good twelve hours after that!'

'I'll remember that.' He laughed. 'Is Emma about? I'd like to say hello.'

This was what she'd been dreading.

'I'm afraid Emma's out.' She flinched, waiting for the outburst. His reaction was the complete opposite to what she had expected, but then, she hadn't told him the whole truth.

'Out? That's marvellous! How did you do it? I've been trying to get her to go out of an evening for ages! Where is she?'

'Gone to the pictures.'

'Aw, Kristina, you don't know how good that makes me feel. Has she gone with a boy?'

'I — ' She hesitated, not knowing how to tell him.

'Don't worry!' He laughed. 'I'm not going to ask you any more questions. I trust you not to let her out with anyone unsuitable! How about you? Are you missing out on your social life?'

'Oh, I'll survive.'

'Look, I don't want you to think I was checking up on you,' he said.

'I don't think that,' she said.

She could always tell him the truth,

but that would have him hot footing it home and for what good reason? He couldn't stop what was happening, or even change it.

'Will you give the girls a kiss for me?' he said. 'And thanks, Kristina. Don't think I don't appreciate what you're doing. I know it must be a pain for you — '

'Why should it be a pain?' she cried, offended. 'I'm having the time of my life! Strange as this may seem to you, Cory, I happen to like being around children! My life doesn't revolve around the office, you know!'

There was a brief silence, then something that sounded suspiciously like a chuckle.

'I'm sorry, Kristina. You always seem so immaculate, so capable and efficient.'

Was that supposed to be a compliment? She thought it over for a moment, then the truth struck her. He thought she was cold! Unfeeling — incapable of affection and without a motherly bone in her body! That was it exactly and probably why he trusted her with his girls!

He knew they'd be safe with her, that she'd gladly hand them back at the end of his week away without having become fond of them!

'If that's all you wanted,' she said huffily.

'I didn't mean to offend you. I simply meant that a young woman like you must have a hundred better things to do than babysit. Let's not argue about it, please, I value your friendship much too much to risk it over something silly.'

Silly? He didn't know the half of it. As for friendship . . .

'All right,' she said. 'I'll tell the girls you called.'

'Thanks, Kristina. 'Bye now, take care.'

He hung up the phone and she listened for a moment to the hissing of the dead line before the dialling tone buzzed in her ear. Gone. As quickly as that. In the blinking of an eye.

She looked at the clock on the wall and clicked her tongue.

Mark Jacobs had promised to have Emma home by nine and it was now half past! Where were they? She slammed the door of the washing machine shut and set the controls, then went through to the lounge and pulled back the curtain.

It was pitch dark outside.

Where had they got to? Why weren't they home?

* * *

Emma, laughing, slipped her hand through her father's arm.

'Wasn't it funny when the film broke down?' she said. 'When all those people at the back started singing! Then when they got it going, they hadn't matched the soundtrack up and it all went wrong!'

'Apart from that, did you enjoy it?' Mark said. He was delighted that Emma had agreed to come out with him! It was a thrill to play at being a father again.

'It was brill.' She grinned. 'Films always look so much better on a big screen, don't they? There's something about seeing everything so big that makes my tummy go all funny!'

'Don't you ever go to the pictures then?' Mark said, picking up the note of wistfulness in her voice and latching on to it.

'No. Dad prefers to get a video out so we can watch it in the comfort of our own home! I think it's so he doesn't have to arrange sitters for Jodie and Amy. It's a bore, not seeing films until they're old hat!'

'That's a shame,' he commented.

'Oh, I don't mind really. Now and then I have some friends round and we get a couple of scary videos out and have a pyjama party! It's OK, so long as we don't wake the girls up, otherwise we can't watch the film because they insist on joining us and if it's something really gruesome, they have nightmares!'

'Must be a pain,' Mark said.

'Oh, they're all right really, as little sisters go.'

'How about friends your own age, is there anyone special?'

'Tracey, I suppose.' She shrugged. 'She's the nearest thing I've got to a best friend, but she's so involved with her horse that she has little time for anything else. She's always out riding — lucky devil!'

They reached the car and Mark quickly unlocked it so they could get out of the cold.

'Want to go somewhere to eat before I take you home?' he said.

'Better not. You told Kristina you'd have me home for nine and it's gone half past. Besides, if she's had trouble with Jodie or Amy, she'll need me. Sometimes they'll only go to sleep for me.'

He hesitated before starting the engine.

'Is that a fact?' he said. 'Do you do much for them'

'I bath them, help Dad buy their clothes — he's hopeless, he'd dress them like little princesses! I suppose I do the kind of things Mum would have done.'

'That's awful, Emma,' Mark said softly. 'A girl your age should be out, having fun with people her own age, not nannying two little girls who aren't even her real sisters.'

'They are!' Emma cried. 'Well, half-sisters. Anyway, how do you know I don't go out?'

'Do you? Do you belong to any clubs?'

She shook her head.

'I could if I wanted to — '

'Then why don't you? You shouldn't feel tied to the house at your age!'

'Oh, you sound just like Dad.' She laughed.

'Emma, I am your dad,' he said quietly, then gunned the engine.

She watched his profile as they drove along, seeing only the dark outline of his face, lit occasionally by street lights as they passed.

It was strange, but she felt close to this man who had been a stranger for so long. They got on so well. She'd even started to wonder what life would have been like if he'd stayed married to her mother. She could certainly see why her mother had fallen in love with him.

He was charming, had a certain charisma and he made her laugh. When he'd first turned up, she'd wanted to hate him. He'd spoken to her of their years together, her early years and she'd refused to remember, not because she couldn't, but because she didn't want to.

Yet memories were flooding back. Things she had, perhaps deliberately, forgotten had sprung into her mind.

Sitting beside him in the car, she was remembering something . . . something which had nothing to do with cars or cinemas.

'Did you used to take me boating on a lake?' she asked suddenly.

She saw the whiteness of his teeth shine in the darkness.

'You remember that?' He sounded amazed, touched.

'I think so,' she said, frowning, trying to force the memory into a clearer picture. 'I remember you yelling at me to sit down!'

'That's right.' He roared with laughter. 'You were such a scamp! Standing up in the boat, trying to reach a duck and her ducklings. The boat was rocking about all over the place and the water was really filthy and smelly! Your mother wouldn't have thanked me if I'd taken you home stinking to high heaven!'

'Why did you go?' Emma asked, the suddeness of her question and the vehemence of her voice taking him by surprise. 'Why did you leave us?'

'I didn't leave you,' he sighed. 'Jo-ann and I realised we weren't compatible. We agreed that we'd both have a better chance of making a new start if we made the break complete.'

'But you didn't have to break from me,' she said, her voice small and sounding very childish.

'I know,' he said. 'Leaving you was the worst mistake of my life. I realise that now. I've missed so much of your growing up years, Emma, but I'm going to make up for that, I promise!

'All I want is the chance to make it up to you for all those lost years.'

He stopped the car outside the house and saw the curtains move.

'Oh, dear,' he said. 'It looks as if we might be in trouble.'

Kristina was almost frantic with worry by the time Mark's car eventually pulled up outside. She hadn't left the window since Cory phoned, watching out, praying for some sight of the car. All kinds of awful things went through her mind, but her relief at seeing them was short lived, soon replaced by anger with Mark for causing her so much worry.

She watched as Emma and Mark jumped out of the car, laughing. How dare they be so happy when she'd been so worried?

She hurried to the front door and opened it just as Emma was reaching out with her own key.

'Where have you been?' her voice shook.

'To the pictures,' Emma answered innocently.

They all went into the lounge where Kristina rounded on Mark.

'You said you'd be back at nine! I checked in the paper and the film was supposed to finish at half past eight . . . so where have you been?'

'We're an hour late.' Mark laughed carelessly. 'An hour! Where's the harm — '

'I've been worried,' Kristina said. 'And your dad called while you were out.'

'The film broke down,' Emma said, sounding close to tears. 'It took them ages to fix it — '

'Couldn't you have phoned?' Kristina turned again to Mark. 'Didn't it ever occur to you that I might be worried? I'm responsible for Cory's girls . . . '

'All right,' Mark said. 'I'm very sorry,

I should have called, I just didn't think. Emma and I were having such a good time.' He looked at Emma and she smiled and Kristina blanched at the intimacy in the look.

'Well, I'm sorry,' Kristina said tightly. 'But I think you'd better leave now, Mr Jacobs and I think it would be best if you didn't see Emma again until Cory gets back from his trip.'

'Oh, Kristina!' Emma cried. 'You can't mean that. It isn't fair!'

'How long will that be?' Mark asked.

'Five or six days — not long,' Kristina said.

'It's ages!' Emma protested. 'You've no right to stop me seeing my father!'

'I think you'd better leave now, Mr Jacobs,' Kristina said.

Emma, with a rebellious look at Kristina, reached up and kissed Mark's cheek.

'Goodbye, Dad,' she said. 'You will come back won't you?'

'Of course I will.' He smiled. 'Be seeing you, Kristina, and . . . I really am sorry for causing you any worry.'

When he'd gone, Emma turned on Kristina, her face twisted with fury.

'How dare you? Who do you think you are? You've no right to forbid me from seeing my own father!'

'Emma, I had to lie to Cory tonight,' Kristina said calmly. 'I don't want to be put in that position again. He trusted me to take proper care of you and that's what I intend to do. I made a mistake allowing you to go out with Mark Jacobs, it's not a mistake I intend to repeat.'

'It wasn't his fault the film broke down!' Emma shouted.

'No, I know that, but ... but I realised I was wrong to let you out with him. I promised Cory — '

'What are you afraid of, Kristina?' Emma's pretty eyes narrowed almost spitefully. She'd changed, in the past few days, incredibly, she'd changed. It was as if suddenly, she was caught between child and young woman, like two waves clashing at the foot of cliffs.

She was passing through a storm and this wasn't her! Kristina knew it wasn't.

'Afraid?' Kristina said. 'What should I have to be afraid of?'

'You're in love with Cory!' Emma cried. 'That's what's wrong with you!'

Mortified, Kristina could only stand and stare at the girl. Emma, as if aware that she'd just gone one step too far, covered her mouth with her hands. If it was that obvious to Emma, then surely other people must have noticed! Perhaps even Cory himself.

The silence stretched between them, then tears sprang into Emma's eyes and began to course down her cheeks.

'I'm sorry, Kristina!' she cried. 'I'm sorry!'

Kristina felt the tension wash away from her at the sight of the young girl's tears and she put her arms out, drew her close.

'Emma, it's awful enough being fourteen, without having to go through all this as well,' she said, stroking Emma's hair.

'Is it?' Emma looked up, her eyes awash with tears, yet full of hope. 'Is it really awful — for everyone?'

'Yes, yes it is,' Kristina said. 'You're stuck halfway between being a child and a grown up woman. I suppose it's all to do with hormones. Sometimes, you feel so mixed up . . . and then this happens and confuses you even more!'

This brought a fresh bout of sobbing from Emma, but Kristina was glad of it. The girl needed to get some of her tangled feelings out.

For her, the crisis had come when she was slightly younger than Emma, but when it had, at least her mother had been there to help her through it.

Emma had no-one. She couldn't talk about her feelings to Cory because he was a man, and even this new father was too much of a stranger to be a confidant.

At last the girl seemed to calm down. Kristina fetched tissues and mopped up her face, noticing that she'd been wearing a little make-up. She wouldn't be fourteen again, she thought, for anything!

'Have you had anything to eat?'

Emma shook her head. 'Just an ice-cream in the cinema. Everyone was getting cross about the film breaking down, so they handed out freebies.'

'Well, I haven't eaten, either.' Kristina grinned. 'Come on, let's fix ourselves a feast! Cory's got enough instant food in that freezer to feed an army.'

'He can't cook.' Emma wrinkled her nose. 'Not very well anyway. The frozen stuff is a stand-by for when his attempts go wrong — which is more often than not.'

'There's nothing worse than a helpless male.' Kristina laughed and to her relief, Emma laughed, too.

'I fancy canneloni,' Emma said. 'With some salad.'

'Canneloni it is, then.' Kristina, putting her arm around Emma and hugging her tight, laughed with relief.

6

'I want you to meet her, Paula,' Mark said. His hazel eyes were shining with happiness and Paula, try as she might, couldn't remember a time when he looked so happy.

'I daresay I will,' Paula said drily.

'You can count on it,' he said confidently. 'Come with me, I want to show you something.'

The apartment above The Smugglers only occupied one floor, although there were further rooms in the attic. Mark only used about two-thirds of the accommodation space.

'In here,' he said, opening a door.

The room was on the corner with a window looking out over the garden to the side and the back.

'A nice room for a young girl, don't you think?' he said.

'Aren't you jumping the gun a bit?' Paula said.

'We get on so well, Paula. We spent one evening together, yet we hit it off just like that.' He clicked his fingers. 'No effort needed, no awkwardness, nothing. She belongs with me, she knows it and I know it. It's just a matter of convincing Cory Elliot.'

'Have you told her about me?'

'A little,' he said. 'Look, I thought we'd leave the walls plain and paint the beams. Then she could have pretty, floral curtains with tie-backs and a flouncy pelmet, and maybe matching bed linen. A nice, pink carpet and book shelves in the alcove here — '

'Does she read?'

'I don't know,' he frowned.

'Does she like flowery things? Some girls don't, particularly teenagers. You'll probably find she's heavily into black and purple. She'll be more interested in racks for her albums than shelves for her books!'

'It's a long time since I was a teenager,' he said, his frown deepening. 'They speak a whole different language these days. Perhaps I should ask her first — see what she wants.'

'If she wants,' Paula said. 'If, Mark, remember that. It has to be her decision. And what about us? We agreed that, because of my age, we shouldn't delay starting a family of our own. Is that going to have to wait?'

'Of course not.' He kissed her lightly on the cheek. 'There's no reason that having Emma here should change our plans at all. She'll fit in with us, she's that kind of girl. You'll like her, Paula. She's friendly, outgoing, intelligent. She's just an all-round nice girl.'

Paula watched as Mark went around the room, looking in corners, making plans in his mind for how it would be.

She felt a twinge of envy. He should be planning a nursery, surely, for their own children? Not that she begrudged this girl her father's love, not at all, but it just made her own position with Mark seem rather more fragile than it should have been.

If conflicts arose between her and

Emma, would Mark feel obliged to take his daughter's side? He just didn't seem to have considered the possible problems that could arise between them at all.

'Mark,' she said. 'You say that Emma's a nice girl,' she began.

'That's right,' he said.

'Wouldn't you also agree then, that at least some of it must be due to her good upbringing?'

He stared at her for a moment, his lips pressed together.

'Don't you think you'd be doing more harm than good to start interfering in her life now?'

'That's utterly ridiculous!'

'Is it? Is Cory Elliot cruel to her?'

'No,' he was forced to admit. 'But I believe he uses her as an unpaid baby-minder! Do you think I want to see my daughter being treated as a skivvy?'

'Of course not,' Paula said. 'But I don't believe that she is! From what you've told me about her, she seems a very happy, well-adjusted girl. Why can't you be content with just working on your relationship with her? Letting her come to stay now and then, visiting her, being a part of her life, but not all of it?'

'That's not enough, Paula.'

'For who? For Emma? Or for you?'

He squared his shoulders, then brushed past her, leaving her to stand in the empty room. She looked around it and thought that yes, yes it was a nice room for a teenage girl and yes, she'd welcome Mark's daughter with open arms if she thought for a moment it was the right thing to do.

Turning on her heel, she followed him into the corridor and touched his shoulder.

'What about her stepfather?' she said. 'Her half-sisters?'

'I think,' he said, 'that it might be best for everyone concerned, if we severed all connections.'

'But that's inhuman!' Paula cried. 'You did that once before and you've admitted that was a mistake.'

'That was different,' he said stubbornly.

One last thing came into her mind then.

'Would you expect Emma to love any children you and I might have?'

'Of course.' He smiled, his face flooding with warmth. He longed to have a family, Paula knew that and she was sure he'd make a good father, loving and kind, but as far as good old-fashioned common sense was concerned, he seemed to have short measure.

'Oh, Mark.' She shook her head sadly. 'Why can't you see?'

★　★　★

Anton Massey might well take good care of his staff, but he didn't believe in wasting money on hotel accommodation, Cory thought, as he tossed and turned in his uncomfortable bed.

While his meetings all took place in

plush surroundings, he was expected to sleep in the cheapest rooms Massey could book!

He sat up and flicked on the light. Paris! He could just as easily be in a dingy back street in London!

The light bulb was so dim that trying to read gave him a headache and the throbbing music pounding up from the nightclub two floors below made listening to music impossible.

He'd showered in cold water before coming to bed, then to find the mattress full of lumps and bumps and the linen scratchy, was adding insult to injury.

His window looked out on a yard filled with over-flowing dustbins where alley cats fought for the scraps thrown out by the hotel restaurant.

At least, he thought, the food was reasonable.

He wondered if the girls were eating properly, especially Amy, who could be a fussy little so-and-so at times.

Smiling to himself, he decided that they were probably eating better than usual. Kristina was a good cook, creative and skilful.

At least, she had been when helping out at birthday parties. She came up with the most beautiful and inventive cakes. A hedgehog for Amy, a cat for Jodie and, more recently, a guitar for Emma!

He always laughed and teased her about her potential for domesticity and she always appeared to be offended, yet, their earlier telephone conversation had changed his mind somewhat. She said she had actually enjoyed taking care of the girls!

He picked up the photograph he'd brought with him and studied it in the dim light. Three girls, sitting one behind the other, Emma at the back, her smile radiant. He thought he'd mind that she looked like her father, but it didn't bother him. She was Emma and he loved her, it was as simple, as cut and dried as that.

As for the other two! Pixies both of them with their huge eyes, little noses and pointy chins!

He wondered what Jo-ann would

make of them now! She'd been almost devastated when she discovered she was expecting Jodie. Jo-ann was a person who liked order in her life and their lives were about as neat and well-ordered as it was possible for them to be.

She worked at the Massey Corporation while Emma was at school and when Cory was home, she was quite happy to let him do the necessary parenting. She wasn't a natural mother at all, but she worked hard at it and when Jodie was born, she tried, she really tried to make a success of it.

And she was managing well when she became pregnant again. This time she was furious, she blamed Cory. Another three years, she said, and Jodie would have been off her hands and at school and she could resume her career, but Jo-ann settled down and started to look forward to the birth of her third child.

Then everything went so horribly wrong.

Cory couldn't understand why she hated being at home instead of work.

He loved it! Never happier than when he was playing games with the girls, or kicking a ball about in the park with them. He even had a bash at cooking — and a bash just about summed up his sometimes pathetic efforts.

He smiled to himself, recalling the faces as he plonked yet another blackened creation in the middle of the table. The little ones would both turn up their noses and Jodie would say, without compunction, 'I'm not eating that!'

But Emma would smile and pick up a spoon.

'Perhaps if we scrape the burned bits off,' she'd say optimistically. 'It might be all right.'

She'd set to, getting rid of the burned crust, then her face would fall and she'd say, 'What was it supposed to be, anyway, Dad?'

He, with his head in the freezer, would call back, 'Lasagne, anyone?'

He laughed out loud. Oh, no, he certainly needn't worry that the girls weren't eating properly! Kristina would see to it that they were.

He put the photograph down and pictured Kristina. She'd been something of a protégée of Jo-ann's. Jo-ann had spotted her potential and had plotted a course for Kristina through the ranks of the Massey Corporation.

She'd been an excellent judge of that, he thought. Kristina was a very clever young woman. Very beautiful, too, he thought, surprised to find himself thinking about her as a woman and not just Kristina Versey.

Perhaps it was a sign, he thought, settling back down beneath the covers. A sign that he was at last getting over losing Jo-ann. A sign that he was ready to take on the world again.

He closed his eyes and fell asleep with a smile on his face.

★　★　★

Mark Jacobs was the last person Kristina expected to find on the doorstep. She thought she'd made herself more than plain to him, but he was carrying a large bunch of flowers, holding them out towards her with a lop-sided grin on his attractive face.

'For me?' she said, blushing.

'A peace offering,' he said. 'I feel terrible about the other night. You must have been worried. It's so long since I did any practical parenting, that I've forgotten the worries and anxieties that go with it.'

'Well, Emma explained about the film breaking down and everything and I guess I did over-react. Your apology is accepted, if you'll accept mine for being so rude.'

'You weren't rude!' he protested. 'Justifiably cross, I'd say. Anyway, can I take it that we're friends now?'

'Of course.' She smiled. 'Look, why don't you come in for a moment?'

He nodded and followed her through to the kitchen. She looked completely different to the woman he'd first met at the Massey building. Her long hair was clipped back in a pony tail and she wore a track suit. He couldn't help thinking that she looked far more at home with herself this way.

'I'm just getting a casserole ready for dinner tonight,' she said. 'Sit down. You don't mind if I continue, do you?'

'Go ahead,' he said. 'It smells wonderful.'

She shook chopped mushrooms in to the pan with the softening onions and frowned at him.

'I'm not going to invite you to join us,' she said sternly.

'I wasn't angling for an invitation.' He laughed at the serious expression on her face. 'Just passing a comment. Did you know Jo-ann?'

'Very well.' She smiled. 'We were good friends. I liked her, she was a really nice person.'

'I know, just the wrong one for me,' he murmured.

'You won't see Emma, you know,' she went on. 'She's at school. And when she does get home, she'll have home-work to do.'

'I know, it was you I came to see. It's quiet here, isn't it?' He looked around for some sign of Jodie and Amy.

'Jodie's at playgroup and Amy's having her morning nap. Why do you want to see me, Mr Jacobs?'

'Mark, please! Things are going well between Emma and I, and I don't want to lose it, which is what I think will happen if we don't continue seeing each other. So, I want to ask you if you'll agree to her spending the day with me at The Smugglers on Sunday? I want her to see the place and to meet my fiancée, Paula.'

'I'm sorry,' Kristina's eyes slid away from his and she began to dice carrots. 'It's not for me to agree or disagree. Something like that is best left to Cory.'

'But he's away.'

'Exactly. I'm not going to agree to anything like that behind his back. It wouldn't be fair. He loves Emma, Mr . . . Mark, he really does. I don't think you really understand how much. You know, whenever she was ill, it was

111

always Cory who stayed home from work to take care of her, not Jo-ann. When I first met them as a family outside of work, I thought that Emma was his child, not Jo-ann's!'

Mark shifted uncomfortably on the stool, then eventually stood up and walked over to the window. He hadn't come to listen to how close Emma and Cory were.

'Nice garden,' he said.

'Oh, that's Emma's handiwork. She loves pottering about out there — and before you say it, I don't see why a girl her age shouldn't enjoy gardening,' Kristina said defensively. 'At her age, I baked cakes!'

He laughed. 'I wasn't going to say anything of the sort,' he said. 'I was going to say she takes after me for that. I've got two acres at The Smugglers — two acres, Miss Versey!'

She banged the lid down on the slow cooker and pushed it to one side, glaring at Mark with openly hostile amber eyes.

'Two acres of land doesn't qualify you as a suitable parent for Emma!'

'You're very protective towards him, aren't you?' he commented.

'It's not that!' she said. 'It just seems terribly sneaky of you to come here while he's away and arrange these things. Why can't you just wait until he comes back?'

'I've waited ten years,' he said. 'That's quite long enough in my book. Does Cory phone?'

'Every day,' she said.

'Then ask him, please.'

'I don't know, I — ' She bit her lip uneasily.

'Please, Miss Versey. If he won't give his permission, then I'll abide by that, I promise you. I'll keep away and you won't have to deal with me again.'

She was hesitating. He seized upon her indecision and pressed home his point.

'You could come along, too, if you like! Bring the little girls with you. We've a playground out the back where they can play safely and you'll find our food really is good. I'd like you to meet Paula, too! Maybe if you see where I live and work, meet my fiancée . . . maybe then you'll accept that I'm really all I say I am.'

Her face, at last, cracked into a somewhat reluctant smile.

'I'll ask him,' she promised. 'Where can I reach you?'

'I'll be at The Smugglers! I've given up taking a hotel room locally, it's only an hour's drive home. Here's one of my cards, actually . . . take a bunch!'

He reached into his pocket and handed Kristina a thick wad of business cards.

'What..?'

'Hand them around your friends.' He grinned. 'We cater for parties, large and small; functions, formal or otherwise! And we do terrific bar meals as well as restaurant food. Plus, we have an unusually extensive wine list and — '

'OK.' She nodded. 'You've convinced me! Well, if that's all you wanted — '

'That's all I wanted.' He smiled. 'Goodbye, Miss Versey. I'll look forward to hearing from you.'

'My name's Kristina,' she said. 'And I'll call you in the morning. Thanks again for the flowers — they're lovely.'

'Ever give you flowers, does he?' Mark asked as they reached the door.

Kristina blushed again.

'He should.' Mark smiled. 'Be seeing you, Kristina.'

Then he was walking back to his car whistling happily as he went.

7

'I don't know who was responsible for booking these rooms.' Cory laughed into the telephone. 'The room I had in Paris was awful — this one is fantastic!'

'I think it was Mr Massey's new secretary,' Kristina said ruefully. 'She does her best, but — '

'Never mind,' Cory said. 'At least her itinerary has been spot on so far! Anyway, this place makes up for Paris — it's wonderful.'

'Is the trip still going well?'

'Perfect, except . . . we've had a bit of a problem. The man I was supposed to meet here has been taken ill and the chap they sent in his place doesn't speak a word of English! What with my rotten Italian and his lousy English, we aren't communicating at all!' He shook his head in disbelief.

'We don't even have a common

language — although between us we can speak seven! So, the meeting has been postponed until tomorrow when we'll have the benefit of an interpreter. I'll be at least a day behind schedule by then, but I've already called ahead and changed my hotel and flight bookings.'

'So you won't be coming home on time?'

'I'm afraid not.'

She sounded disappointed. Was she, he wondered? On her behalf — or for the girls' sake? Or had she simply had enough of babysitting?

'How are things at home?' he asked.

'Fine . . . ' she answered uneasily.

He sensed her hesitation. 'But?' he asked.

'Cory, I don't like having to put this on you when you're so far away, but I haven't much choice. It's Mark Jacobs — ' She waited for an exasperated sigh, but nothing came.

'He's been to see Emma again and . . . he wants to take her to his home for the day on Sunday. I gather he wants her to see where he lives and meet his fiancée. I said I couldn't possibly agree without your say-so.'

'I see,' Cory murmured. 'How does Emma feel?'

'I haven't spoken to her yet,' Kristina said. 'I thought I should speak to you first. He . . . em . . . he invited me and Jodie and Amy, too.'

'All right.' Cory smiled. He looked at the photograph of his three girls and trusted in Emma's happy smile. 'Why not? If Emma's happy about going, then I've no objections.'

'You don't?' Kristina gasped. 'I thought you'd be dead set against the idea.'

'A week ago, yes I would have,' he admitted. 'But I've had a lot of time to think while I've been away. Long nights, boring journeys. It's Emma's life and I have no right to stop her living it as she wishes. Very soon she'll be old enough to leave home anyway. I'd hate her to be put in the position of deciding between Mark and I, but if it comes to that, then it's a decision she alone can make. If I make it for her, she may never forgive me. I can't put her through all the trauma of court appearances and messy custody proceedings! Ye Gods, it'd be worse than a divorce case!'

'I'll be there, with her all the time,' Kristina said.

'I'm glad,' he said softly. 'Thanks, Kristina, for all you've done, all that you're doing.'

'Oh, it's nothing — '

'It's everything to me,' he said. He wanted to say more, so much more.

'Oh, Emma's here . . . she wants to say hello.'

There was no time for him to say goodbye to Kristina before Emma came on to the line.

'Hi, Dad! Where are you? Italy? You will remember to bring us something back . . . We haven't had any postcards yet.'

'I've posted lots.' He laughed. 'They'll probably all arrive after I've come home.'

He felt as if he were being torn apart.

His eyes stung, his heart pounded. It would break his heart if Emma left to live with her real father, but if he prevented her from doing that, if that was what she wanted, he could lose her for ever and he wouldn't want that.

'How's school?'

'Boring!'

'You don't mean that!'

'I've been chosen to play a clarinet solo in the school concert,' she admitted shyly. 'It's not for another month, so you'll be able to come and see me.'

'Great,' he said. 'I'll look forward to it. I'll have to go now, love. Give your sisters a kiss from me.'

'I will, Daddy. I love you!' she said excitedly.

'I love you, too,' he said and the line went dead.

He put the phone down and buried his face in his hands. She hadn't called him Daddy for years! He rubbed tears away and tried not to think about Sunday, where she'd be, who she'd be with.

He tried not to, but thinking of Sunday kept him awake all night, despite the comfort of his room.

★   ★   ★

By Sunday, it was raining and the sky was hidden behind a thick mass of black cloud. Kristina caught her breath as she turned into the car park at The Smugglers.

The building stood among an assortment of Victorian, fisherman's cottages and Georgian town houses. A higgledy piggledy arrangement of styles, which somehow blended together as if it had always been intended that way. Roofs narrow and wide, tall and low, stood out bright against the darkness of the sky.

To the front, the inn looked out across a pink, brick-tiled road which gave way to a cobbled path which stopped at the edge of the green. Farther downhill, over the roofs of other houses, she could see the sea, leaden and fearsome.

The Smugglers itself was old, very old and Kristina sensed its atmosphere as soon as she walked through the low doorway into the large bar room. The ceilings were surprisingly high, black-beamed and strung with nautical and equine instruments from long ago. Gleaming horse brasses hung on leather straps against the off-white walls.

Emma gasped.

'It's so old!' she said.

'It must seem especially so to you.' Kristina smiled.

'Emma!' Mark appeared and hurried forward to greet them, holding out his hands and taking Emma's in a gesture of greeting. 'Welcome to The Smugglers! Sorry about the rain! I wish you'd been able to see it in the sunshine.'

'It's a wonderful place, Mark,' Kristina commented. 'I can see why you fell in love with it.'

'I think, a guided tour is in order,' Mark said happily and led the way, with Emma holding his arm. Kristina bringing up the rear with Jodie and Amy, heard warning bells clanging in her ears, but she was helpless. There was nothing she could do to stop the unthinkable happening.

'This is the restaurant,' Mark said as they went through another low door-way. 'We do a steady trade, but I'm looking forward to the summer season. Things should really take off then.'

He picked up a menu.

'Here, take a look. See if anything takes your fancy and I'll order it now so we can eat at one.'

'How can you do such a wide range of food?' Kristina cried.

'Ah,' Mark said confidently.

'I manage that with the help of the deep freeze, an obliging local butcher and a very reliable fisherman!'

Kristina pondered the menu with the girls and sighed.

'I think chicken for Jodie and Amy, dressed crab for me and . . . Emma?'

'Oh, crab for me, too, please,' Emma said distractedly.

'Excuse me,' Mark hurried through a

door marked private, returning a few moments later.

'It's too wet for us to go outside, so why don't we go upstairs? We've been renovating the apartment and it's only half done, but it's comfortable enough.'

He's trying very hard, Kristina thought, too hard perhaps. Almost as if he's trying to sell himself. For the first time, she felt a pang of sympathy for him. His position was an unenviable one.

Upstairs, in front of a blazing fire, they met Paula. Kristina's first impression was of a tall, rather forbidding woman with flaming, auburn hair and flashing green eyes, but when she spoke, Paula possessed a remarkably soft and gentle voice.

Mark flitted through the introductions then went to a hostess trolley laid with coffee and cakes.

'So, you're Emma,' Paula said, smiling at the teenager. 'It's lovely to meet you at last. Mark's told me such a lot about you.'

'I'm afraid you've got an advantage over me, then,' Emma replied with the forthrightness of her youth. 'All I know is your name and that you're going to marry him!'

'Ah, well, we'd best put that right then,' Paula said, completely unruffled. Used to dealing with children and awkward teenagers, perhaps?

'My name is Paula Conway and I'd be happy if you'd call me Paula . . . that goes for all of you.' She included the whole party with a sweep of her eyes. 'Up until a year ago, I was a nursing sister in a hospital in Egypt. That's where I met Mark. Somehow — I still don't quite know how — he persuaded me to come here with him and help run The Smugglers.

'So far.' She shrugged her shoulders and smiled contentedly and lovingly at Mark. 'So far, I'm certain my decision was the right one. It's a completely different way of life for me, but . . . I have to say I do miss nursing and I'm toying with the idea of returning to work part-time at the local hospital.

'Any questions?'

Emma laughed and shook her head. Kristina could see that she liked Paula with her generous smile and sparkling eyes, but did she view her seriously as a potential stepmother?

'Paula's being very modest about what she's done here,' Mark put in. 'She's been the driving force behind a lot of the renovations. I couldn't have done it without her.'

'You're very quiet, little ones.' Paula turned her attention to the two little, blonde girls. 'What can I get you to drink? Would you like some fizzy lemonade?'

She looked to Kirstina for approval. Kristina nodded.

'Just a little, then.' Paula's smile grew broader. 'We don't want to fill your little tummies up with bubbles!'

Mark had drawn Emma to one of the windows. The room was big, stretching from the back of the building, to the front, partially divided by a beamed opening. Originally, it had probably been at least two rooms, possibly up to four.

'You can't see much when it's raining, but on a sunny day, there's a lot going on. Jet skiers and windsurfers off the beach that way, fishing boats down towards the harbour. It's a smashing beach, Emma, sandy and soft and it's quite safe to swim.'

Putting his arm around her shoulders, he led her to a window overlooking the back garden.

'And that's my garden.' He grinned as Emma gasped.

'A bit of a mess, I know,' he admitted. 'But we've been concentrating our efforts on the building. It goes back a long way and towards the end, it widens out and takes in a small stream and an orchard. I was hoping to be able to show you round it, but it's far too wet today.'

'It makes our garden look so small,' Emma said.

'I've plans for that land, Emma,'

Mark said, his eyes glittering.

Kristina was watching, listening. She felt distinctly uneasy.

'I'm going to have a small beer garden, but beyond that . . . Well, I thought a pony. Do you like to ride, Emma?'

What girl doesn't? Kristina thought crossly.

Emma was nodding enthusiastically.

'We'll have to see what we can do for you then,' Mark promised.

Paula caught Kristina's eye and the two women exchanged understanding looks. He was desperately trying to buy the girl! Couldn't he see he was wrong to go about things that way?

'A pony — of my own?' Emma cried and the light in her eyes said that it was something she'd always dreamed off. Kristina bit back her anger, saving it for later.

'Why not?' Mark was saying in a tone that implied he'd give her anything, anything at all. 'They hold a monthly auction in a village a couple of miles from here. I'll take you sometime.

'Come on,' he said. 'I'll show you the rest of the apartment.'

Kristina made to follow them, but Paula placed a restraining hand on her arm.

'You mustn't mind Mark,' she said. 'He's so eager to do what's right by Emma that he's become blind to the way he's behaving. I know it must appear to you that he's trying to buy her — '

'That's exactly how it appears to me,' Kristina retorted, her eyes flashing.

'You're wrong,' Paula said. 'So wrong. He isn't trying to buy her at all. Can't you see what he's trying to do?'

'Frankly? No, I can't.'

'He's trying to make up to her for ten lost years. He feels guilty because it took him so long to get himself together and finally get in touch.'

'So that makes it all right for him to come along and break up a happy family,' Kristina lowered her voice, mindful of the two little girls.

'I know how you must feel,' Paula

said. 'And I do sympathise, but what can I do? I've tried to talk to him, but he's so single-minded. He gets an idea in his head and goes all out for it. Like this place.' She spread her hands.

'It was his dream. You should have seen it when he first showed it to me. It was virtually falling down. Builders he consulted said nothing could be done, but he kept on until he found one who said he'd try!

'And this is the result. He gets what he wants, Kristina, and I'm afraid that right now, he wants his daughter.'

Kristina pressed her lips together.

'And I suppose he thinks he's going to get her?' she said.

'He's not a bad man, Kristina, he — '

'Excuse me.' Kristina didn't want to listen to any more. She brushed past Paula and hurried out of the room into the long corridor. At the far end, she could hear Emma laughing. She hurried along, following the sound.

In a room at the end, on a corner, windows facing side and back, Emma sat cross-legged on a dust sheet on the floor. Open in front of her was a book of fabric samples.

'This?' she said.

Mark pulled a disgusted face.

'Black and pink stripes! Oh, Emma! Are you colour blind or something?'

Emma's laughter pealed out again.

'Well, you wouldn't let me have the purple aztec pattern!'

'Can't you choose something feminine and chintzy?' Mark said despairingly.

'Yuk,' was Emma's answer to that.

Kristina cleared her throat loudly and Emma scrambled to her feet, an almost guilty look on her face.

'Emma's just deciding how she'd like this room,' Mark said casually.

'Was she?' Kristina said icily.

'Well, she may as well have the room the way she likes it.' He shrugged, still wearing his infuriating smile. 'She's the one who's going to have to sleep in it!'

'Emma,' she said coolly. 'Your coffee is getting cold. You did want coffee, didn't you?'

'Oh, yes.' Emma, with an apologetic smile at her father, hurried out of the room and Kristina took the opportunity to turn on Mark as he made to follow her.

'Just a moment,' she said. 'I'd like a word.'

'What about . . . or can I guess?'

'I thought we were coming here so that Emma could meet Paula and see over this place. I didn't realise you were going to be making plans!'

'I've never made any secret of the fact that I want Emma home with me, where she belongs.' He was still smiling, but his eyes were cold, determined. 'You've seen how well we get on for yourself! If Cory Elliot wants to retain custody of my daughter, then I promise you, he'll have a fight on his hands.'

8

He was going home tomorrow! Home. Such a welcoming, warm word. No more impersonal hotel rooms at night and the faces of strangers during the day. And the trip had gone better than he anticipated. The Europeans were queuing up to invest in the Massey Corporation.

He'd bought the girls a small gift in each country he'd visited and that remained his final task now that he had concluded his business in Amsterdam.

One last shopping trip — and something special for Kristina. She'd been great, although since Sunday, she'd appeared distant whenever he spoke to her on the telephone, almost as if she were hiding something. It worried him. He felt a little off-colour himself and decided to get the shopping done in case he started to feel worse.

Out in the streets of Amsterdam, he searched the shops for gifts for his girls. Emma was easily catered for. He'd bought her a doll in national dress for each country he'd visited. She was too old to play with dolls, but at an age to appreciate them for their ornamental value.

The little Dutch doll, with her yellow pigtails and wooden clogs, had been hand crafted, the features on her face hand painted. Yes, he thought, Emma would love this. It was something she could keep for ever.

For Jodie, it had to be a little weather house. A Dutch boy with an umbrella for when it rained, a girl with a sunny smile, in a pretty dress, for good days.

And for Amy, a soft-bodied doll.

He enjoyed shopping for gifts and the final gift was, perhaps, the most important of all. Something for Kristina, for her patience and kindness and her sensible good advice which he'd come to take for granted, but not any more — after this, there would be no more taking

Kristina for granted.

His eye was caught by a display of Delft ware goods ranging from slim, blue bud-vases to intricately designed plates. He'd wanted to bring her flowers, but those could come from anywhere and wouldn't last long.

A flower vase should last for ever.

He steered away from the designs aimed at the tourists, picturing Dutch towns, windmills and tulips and chose instead a small, rounded vase, perfect for large-headed flowers. It was predominantly white with a blue pattern around the neck made up of intertwined hearts. When he got home, he'd buy her flowers . . .

Then he went to another shop and bought perfume.

He hadn't bought perfume since . . .

Deliberately, he kept away from Jo-ann's favourite fragrances and with the help of the assistant chose something light and slightly flowery with a subtle exotic tang — perfect for Kristina.

Outside in the street, pleased with his

purchases, he strode off in the direction of his hotel. He was like a man walking on air until the pain struck him. He had to stop, lean against a wall.

He'd been feeling unwell all day, but had put his queasiness down to strange surroundings and a hectic schedule involving a lot of travel, but this pain was very real and far more frightening than the niggling aches he'd been experiencing.

Sweat broke out on his face and someone passing him muttered about the disgrace of being drunk on the streets of Amsterdam.

He tried to call for help, but no sound would come. The pain took him to his knees. Forcing his mind to focus, he tried again to call for help, reaching out with his hand this time to a passing woman.

Thank goodness he could speak Dutch, he thought, as he tried to explain his predicament, but it wasn't necessary. Her English was perfect.

'Don't worry,' she said, smiling. 'I will call an ambulance.'

She turned then and spoke to some

other people in Dutch. It was all becoming a blur. Cory wanted to thank her, but when he looked up, all he saw was an undulating sea of faces staring down at him with a mixture of fear and curiosity.

His last thoughts before he passed out were, I don't want to die! Not here on the street — my girls — my girls . . .

★ ★ ★

Shaking, Kristina put the phone down.

'Who was it?' Emma's eyes were huge, her face pale. 'Is it about Daddy? What's happening?'

Kristina shook herself.

'He won't be coming home tomorrow as planned, he — he's been taken ill. He's in hospital in Amsterdam.'

'What's wrong with him? Did they say?' Emma cried.

'They're not sure.'

'We'll have to go to him!' Emma declared.

'No,' Kristina said quickly. 'I'll go, I

think you should all stay here, you and the girls.'

She didn't want to take Emma in case . . .

She swallowed hard. If the worst should happen, then it was better Emma was here, at home, in familiar surroundings. What was she thinking? Nothing awful was going to happen to Cory — it just couldn't!

'I'm going next door to see Mrs Willis,' she said calmly. 'When I come back, I'll see about getting on a flight tonight. Try not to worry, Emma. I'm sure he'll be all right. He's probably eaten something a bit iffy, that's all.'

Mrs Willis shook her head when Kristina relayed the news.

'Such a shame, especially after what happened to Jo-ann,' she said. 'I'd help if I could, but my husband is ill and I can't leave him. Although . . . ' her face broke into a smile. 'I could have Jody and Amy around here, but I haven't the room for the three of them.'

'That's great help, Mrs Willis, thank

you so much,' Kristina said. 'I'll fetch them round.'

Back home, she asked Emma to pack some things for the girls.

'What about me?' Emma said. 'What am I going to do?'

'You'll have to come with me,' Kristina said. 'Unless I can think of something better — so pack a case for yourself, too, and see if you can find your passport. I'll get on to the airport.'

'Thanks, Kristina!' Emma flung her arms around Kristina and kissed her cheek, almost knocking her off her feet. Her exuberance was short-lived. As they left for the airport, she was suddenly seized by uncertainty and stopped in her tracks.

'Hurry, Emma,' Kristina called from the car. 'What's keeping you?'

Tears spilled on to the younger girl's face.

'I'm frightened,' she cried. 'Oh, Kristina, I couldn't bear it if anything happened to him!'

'It won't!' Kristina said firmly, wishing she felt as certain as she sounded.

★ ★ ★

Hospitals never sleep, but when Kristina and Emma arrived, the building was silent. They stepped from the cab, Kristina paid the driver — too much, she was too worried to concentrate on trivial things like money. She glanced at Emma and the younger girl slid her hand into hers.

'He'll be all right,' Kristina whispered. 'I can feel it, can't you?'

'I don't know,' Emma shuddered. 'I don't feel anything except scared.'

'Come on.' Kristina smiled. 'We'll soon find out.'

The morning was cold, cloudy, cheerless as they entered the hospital building. It had been a long night, their flight had been delayed by bad weather and they'd spent most of the night in the airport lounge.

Kristina approached the reception desk.

'I believe Cory Elliot was brought in here late yesterday afternoon — '

'Ah, Mrs Elliot.' The receptionist on duty spoke perfect English. 'We've been expecting you. This way, please.'

'But, I — ' Kristina started to protest, then when the receptionist turned enquiring eyes upon her, she shrugged. 'It doesn't matter.'

For the moment, it was probably best to let them go on believing that she was Cory's wife. Emma hadn't noticed, she was lost in a world of her own.

'Take a seat here.' The woman smiled. 'Someone will be along to talk with you very soon.'

'How is he . . . ?' Kristina put out her hand. 'Do you know?'

'I'm sorry.' The woman shook her head sadly. 'I was only told to ask you to wait. Please sit down. I'll arrange for some coffee for you.'

'Thank you.' Kristina sat down beside Emma.

She looked at the girl. Emma was as white as a sheet, her eyes ringed with black shadows. Little wonder, she hadn't slept at all and exhaustion always makes things seem worse. They'd broken their journey from the airport only to drop their luggage at the hotel, not stopping to clean up or change their clothes.

She tried to think of words of comfort, but none came to mind that she hadn't already spoken at least twice over and such words were beginning to sound so clichéd and hackneyed even to herself that she felt sure Emma must be sick of hearing them.

At last, a door farther along the silent corridor opened and a doctor came towards them. He was tall, thin, with white-blonde hair and piercing, blue eyes.

'Mrs Elliot.' He smiled, extended his hand. 'I'm Doctor Van Helfteren.'

He pulled a chair round and sat right in front of Emma and Kristina. He's smiling, Kristina thought, he's smiling so the news can't be bad.

'I'm not Mrs Elliot,' Kristina said and the doctor frowned, puzzled. 'I'm Kristina Versey, a . . . a friend of the family. Mr Elliot is a widower and this is his daughter, Emma.'

'I see.'

'I've been staying with Cory's girls while he's been over here on business. How is he, Doctor?'

'His condition is stable,' the doctor said. 'He collapsed in the street yesterday and was brought here, suffering with appendicitis. We operated in the early hours of this morning and all went well, but, the infection was severe and recovering is going to take rather longer than you might normally expect for such a routine operation.'

'But he's all right?' Emma whispered.

'Certainly,' Dr Van Helfteren beamed. 'He is a very strong, very healthy man. Obviously, I should not care to have him moved for at least four to five days, but then I am sure he could be transferred to a hospital in England.'

'Can we see him?' Emma asked.

'Just for a moment. He is still sleeping and you may find his appearance a little alarming, but I assure you, he is perfectly all right.'

Emma nodded understanding and as

they followed the doctor, she slipped her hand again into Kristina's. They squeezed hands, exchanged limp smiles and entered a small side ward.

Cory was asleep, very pale and an i.v. drip fed into his hand.

A nurse smiled at them encouragingly.

'He looks so ill.' Emma's voice shook.

They moved closer to the bed. Kristina could hear her own heart pounding, blotting out everything else. She wanted to reach out . . . touch him, but she was afraid of being overwhelmed by her own feelings.

His head moved. He muttered in his sleep. The nurse hurried forward, nodded at Kristina.

She moved closer.

His mouth formed one word, so soft that only Kristina could hear it. It took a few moments for her to realise that it was her own name.

'Kristina . . . '

Then he settled again, back into his deep sleep.

'Why don't you get some rest now?' the doctor said. 'Come back this afternoon. He will be able to speak to you then.'

Kristina nodded and with one last, wistful look at the man lying helpless and vulnerable on the bed, she led Emma back into the corridor . . .

Emma fell asleep almost as soon as she lay down on the bed. Kristina could not sleep. She kept hearing over and over again her name on Cory's lips. It meant nothing, she told herself. He was probably worried about his girls, that was all.

Emma slept for several hours, then woke at lunchtime, feeling hungry.

'I've sent down for some sandwiches.' Kristina laughed. 'I thought you might be hungry.'

'Did you get any sleep?' Emma was far more cheerful now as she searched through her hastily-packed bag for clean clothes.

'A little,' Kristina lied. Emma looked at the bed beside hers, still neatly made.

'You should have got some sleep,' she said. 'We saw that Dad's all right!'

'Emma, as soon as we've seen him and spoken to him, we'll have to go home. Mr Willis is unwell and it's unfair to expect Mrs Willis to take care of Jodie and Amy. They're enough of a handful under normal circumstances.

'And, Emma — '

Emma was vigorously brushing her hair. She stopped and looked levelly at Kristina.

'Yes?'

'I . . . I think it would be best if you don't say too much about Mark Jacobs.'

'Can't I tell him about *The Smugglers?* And Paula?'

'Just . . . just prune it a little, eh?'

'If you say so.' Emma shrugged. 'I can tell him about my room and the pony when he's better though, can't I?'

A little girl again, Kristina thought. What a confusing age Emma was, not just for herself, but for the adults who cared about her, too.

'Yes, when he's better.' Kristina

forced a smile. She hadn't dared ask Emma outright how she'd feel about moving in with her father for good. She feared Emma's answer much too much.

That afternoon at the hospital, Cory was sitting up in bed. He still had the i.v. drip, but there was colour in his cheeks and a wide grin on his face. He'd been moved into a small ward.

'Hi! Thanks for coming, but you shouldn't have come all this way! I hear you called in to see me earlier.'

Emma and Kristina exchanged glances and both burst out laughing.

'What's so funny?'

'We were so worried.' Kristina laughed. 'It's good to see you looking human again.'

She leaned forward and kissed his cheek and Emma followed suit.

'Did they tell you what happened?' Cory said. He sounded like a little boy, about to relate an exciting adventure.

'Just that you've had your appendix removed,' Kristina said.

'I collapsed in the street! People

thought I was drunk — and all I'd had to drink all day was coffee. I hadn't eaten anything because I felt a bit queasy, but I had no idea anything like this would happen.

'I came round as they were putting me in the ambulance — I don't remember mind you, somone told me this — and I starting yelling that I'd left my shopping behind on the pavement! So I was rushed to hospital along with my carrier bags!'

'Oh, Dad.' Emma shook her head. 'Fancy worrying about your stupid shopping when you were so ill!'

'Stupid shopping, eh?' He laughed. 'I'll have you know that there were presents in those bags. You wouldn't have thanked me if I'd come home without them, would you?'

Emma looked hurt by his remark, even though he was obviously joking.

'I don't care about presents,' she said. 'As long as you come home safe.'

'Aw, love, I'm sorry.' He reached out and squeezed her hand. 'You must have been worried. I'm glad Kristina brought you with her, though. It's cheered me up no end to see you. Where are the other two?'

'With Mrs Willis,' Kristina said. 'That's why we really must fly back to England this afternoon. Mr Willis has been ill and — '

'Of course,' Cory cried. 'Yes, you must go back immediately. I'll be fine — as you can see.'

Although he was cheerful, Kristina could see lines of strain etched around his mouth and eyes.

'We're tiring you,' she said. 'Emma just wanted to see that you were all right. We didn't know how seriously ill you were.'

'I'm sorry for worrying you.' He smiled. 'I didn't ask you about your day out on Sunday, Em!' he said.

'Oh, it was all right.' Emma shrugged and Cory pulled a face.

'Surely, it was better than all right,' he said.

'Well, it was fun actually,' Emma

conceded with a laugh. 'It's right by the sea and there's a huge garden. And Paula's nice — '

'And you get on well with Mark?'

She nodded. 'He's really nice, Dad.'

'Has he said any more about you going to live with him?'

Emma's eyes clouded. She glanced at Kristina.

'He's asked me to think about it,' she said at last.

'Just remember this.' Cory smiled and gripped Emma's hand tightly. 'I'll abide by your decision, whatever it is, but if you want to stay with me, I'll fight tooth and nail to make sure you do! I love you, Emma and I don't want to lose you. I'm on your side, remember that.'

He looked into her serious, hazel eyes.

'I will.' Emma blushed and Kristina felt glad in a way that it was out in the open, although she would rather it had waited until Cory was well again.

Cory's eyes were closing. Kristina put her finger to her lips.

' 'Bye, Daddy,' Emma whispered, kissing the top of Cory's head. His only response was a brief, flickering smile.

'I'm just going to talk to the doctor,' Kristina said. 'Then we'll make arrangements to go back home. We're becoming regular jet-setters aren't we?'

'European commuters!' Emma agreed, giggling.

9

In just twenty-four hours, the strain was beginning to tell on Mrs Willis. Taking care of two young children and an ailing husband had taken it out of her.

'How is Cory?' she asked and Kristina quickly filled her in while Emma got the girls ready to take home.

'I'm glad it's nothing serious,' Kristina said. 'Imagine if he'd collapsed in his hotel room and hadn't been found until morning! Oh, it doesn't bear thinking about. He'd been feeling off colour all day, but put it down to something he'd — Oh, here they are!'

'Kristina!' Little Amy held out her chubby arms and Kristina lifted her up.

'She's very fond of you,' Mrs Willis commented with a smile. 'They all are! But they're good for me. They're all good girls — a real credit to their dad.'

'Well, it was good of you to help us.

Is Mr Willis any better?'

'Happier! He likes having little ones around, but it does tire him. Please don't let that stop you bringing them round to see us, though. I'll soon tell you if they get too much!'

Kristina thanked her again and handed her a bottle of brandy and some chocolates.

'A little thank you,' she said. 'But Cory will thank you properly when he gets home, I'm sure.'

'Naughty girl, that's not necessary! What are friends for ... Oh!' She looked at the chocolates. 'I'm going to enjoy those! I'm sure Alex will enjoy the brandy, too! When will Cory be home?'

'I'm going back to Amsterdam on Friday. He'll have to stay in the cottage hospital here for a while when he gets back, to recuperate properly.'

'Well, at least he'll be home! And if you'd like me to have the girls anytime, Kristina, you've only to say.'

'I think you've done enough,' Kristina said, for despite Mrs Willis's cheerful face, she looked tired and weary. If the worst came to the worst, she'd take all three of them to Holland with her rather than put on poor Mrs Willis again.

'Come along then, say thank you to Mrs Willis and we'll get home.'

Next door, once they were all settled down, Emma joined Kristina in the kitchen.

'Will Mrs Willis have the girls when we go to bring Dad home?'

Kristina shook her head. 'I don't think so. Didn't you notice how tired she looked? She has trouble getting around now with her bad arthritis and looking after Mr Willis is taking it out of her. It's unfair to expect her to look after two boisterous, little girls as well.'

Kristina thought of her own mother and knew she'd willingly come and take care of the girls, but she'd be strange to them and four hundred miles was a long way to come for a few hours babysitting.

'It's a shame you've no relatives nearby who — '

'But I have!' Emma exclaimed. 'My father! I'm sure he'd love to have them and they got on ever so well with Paula.'

'Oh, no,' Kistina said. 'They don't know Paula and Mark well enough to spend a whole day, perhaps a whole night with them. They were happy at the Smugglers before because we were there.'

'Then I'll stay there, too,' Emma declared. 'They'll be fine with me and I don't want Dad coming home alone. I'll go and give him a ring straight away — '

'Leave it until the morning, Emma,' Kristina said. 'Please.'

She needed time to think. It was an ideal solution, the only solution . . . but would Cory agree? Or shouldn't she even put it to him? No, she decided, it had to be her decision, it was unfair to expect Cory to control things from his hospital bed! Every day at work, she made decisions, important decisions, yet here she was plagued with doubt

155

over something as simple as a spot of babysitting!

In the end, the decision was taken from her hands.

'I've called him,' Emma came back into the room. 'He says he's sorry to hear Dad's ill and he'd love to help any way he can! See, Kristina, I told you he'd help.'

★　★　★

Paula Conway enjoyed the chance to look after Cory's girls. She'd always enjoyed working with children and knew exactly how to deal with them. Besides, it gave Mark more time alone with Emma. After all, it wasn't Amy and Jodie who interested him . . .

With the little ones sitting cross-legged on the floor in front of the television set, Paula moved to the window and looked out.

Mark had already begun work on the beer garden. He'd done a lot of the heavy work himself and they were waiting for contractors to come and lay the concrete and slabs. At least this time, for Emma's visit, it wasn't raining, she thought, then caught a glimpse of Mark and Emma in the garden and began to wish that it was.

Mark was waving his arms about expansively as he always did when he was outlining his plans. Paula smiled. Emma seemed to be hanging on to his every word. He was still going on about that wretched pony! He was always so enthusiastic about everything — so much so, that he usually managed to catch everyone else up with him.

When he'd brought her to The Smugglers, all she'd seen was a bleak, ramshackle old house with broken windows and holes in the roof, but within minutes, Mark had conjured up a picture so vivid, that she couldn't help but fall in love with it, too. And he'd done everything he said he was going to do — and more, much more.

And now he wanted Emma.

With a sigh, she turned back to the girls.

'I think it's time for your bath and then off to bed.' She smiled. 'We want to be up nice and early tomorrow so we can go and see Daddy at the hospital.'

They'd already decided not to meet him off the plane and the hospital staff had confirmed that they'd allow the children in to see their father as soon as he was settled.

'Where's Emma?' Jodie got up. 'Emma baths us.'

'Well, I can do it today, can't I?'

Amy stood up and slid her hand into Jodie's. Although two years separated them, they looked so alike.

'I'll make lots of bubbles!' Paula smiled. 'How's that?'

Two identical, lower lips jutted out. Paula shrugged. It didn't matter. They'd been happy with her most of the day and surely Emma and Mark had had enough of each other's company by now. She looked out again, relieved to see them making their way back to the house.

'Here she comes.' She turned her

back to the girls. 'I'll run the bath and Emma can bath you, OK? And I'll tell you what, I'll still make it extra bubbly for you, how's that?'

Two identical smiles made Paula want to gather them both in her arms and hug them! She didn't, knowing they'd probably be mortified at such a blatant display of affection from a stranger . . .

'Yes, of course I'll bath them.' Emma smiled. 'I always do.'

'Wouldn't you like a rest from all that, Emma?' Mark said sympathetically.

Emma looked at him as though he were mad.

'I enjoy bathing them,' she said and taking them both by the hand, hurried off in the direction of the bathroom.

'Well.' Paula smiled wrily. 'That was telling you!'

'Nonsense,' Mark said huffily. 'She should enjoy being a teenager!'

'She does, in her own way,' Paula said, then sighed. 'Oh, it's no use talking to you. You've made up your mind that she's some poor, hard-done-by little waif and nothing will sway you. When are you going to face the fact that she was perfectly happy with her life, until — '

'Until I came along?' Mark's eyebrows rose. 'I rest my case.'

Gales of laughter wafted along the ancient corridors from the bathroom, startling Mark.

'What's going on?' he said.

'That's just Emma and her sisters.' Paula hid her smile. 'Enjoying themselves!'

'Ah.' Mark grinned and put his arm around Paula, pulling her close. 'That could be our family in there, in a few years' time!'

'I hope so.' Paula smiled. 'Two girls and a boy, that's what I'd like!'

'We've already got one girl,' Mark said and Paula instantly stiffened in his arms.

'No,' she said. 'We haven't any children. Emma is almost grown-up

— she doesn't *belong* to anyone!'

'She belongs *with* me,' he said. 'You should have heard her in the garden — she loves this place! Once Cory Elliot is back on his feet, she'll be moving in here, which reminds me, I must do something definite with that room. When she does come for good, I want her to have her own, proper room, not a guest room!'

They lapsed into silence.

His was a smiling silence in which he looked forward to a rosy future with his rediscovered daughter. Hers a brooding one in which she seriously began to doubt Mark's love for both her and his daughter.

Whatever he might say about Emma's lack of proper childhood, wasn't it his own conscience that troubled him? Didn't he see spoiling Emma as a means of salving that troublesome conscience of his?

In a little while, the laughter stopped and they heard Emma taking the little girls to the guest room.

'Now she's putting them to bed,'

Mark grumbled.

'It's part of being a family, Mark! Oh, all right, I'll do it,' Paula sighed, giving him a black look. 'We can't have your precious daughter missing ten minutes with her loving father now, can we?'

He stared after her, startled by her uncommonly harsh attitude. She came back five minutes later, her expression softer, her eyes misty.

'I think you'd better come with me,' she said. 'Quietly, Mark.'

Taking his hand she led him along the corridor.

She pushed open the door of the guest bedroom a crack. Emma was sitting squashed in the middle of a single bed with one sister on each side, an arm around each of them. She was telling them a story and they were gazing up at her, hanging on her every word.

At times they giggled. Other times, their little faces grew grave and solemn. Beside her, Paula felt Mark swell with pride.

At the end of the story, Emma got out of her bed and the two little ones snuggled down. She bent down and gave each one a kiss.

'Night, night,' she whispered. 'Sleep tight. I love you!'

'I love you,' Jodie said.

'I love you,' Amy repeated.

'Now go straight to sleep, because we'll be seeing Daddy tomorrow! Won't that be wonderful?'

'Yes!' they cried.

'Oh, you scamps, I really do love you!' Emma reached out and gathered them both tightly to her. 'I really, really do!'

Paula, a satisfied smile on her face, turned to look at Mark.

He glared at her then he turned abruptly and hurried off down the corridor.

At the cottage hospital, a private room had been set aside for Cory's recovery.

'This can't be right!' He turned to Kristina.

'Compliments of Mr Massey.' She laughed. 'You see, he's not such a mean, old skinflint after all!'

'Thanks for coming to get me, Kristina,' he said soberly. 'I mean it. I couldn't have faced that flight on my own. I still feel a bit — '

'Of course you do!' Kristina said as two nurses settled Cory into the bed. 'You need lots of rest. Mark will be bringing the girls along in two or three hours, which gives you time to catch up on some sleep.'

Too tired to argue, Cory did exactly that. Kristina stayed with him in the room, sitting in a chair in the corner, watching him sleep. She loved him, she knew that now, yet she felt she'd let him down in the worst possible way.

If Emma decided her future was with Mark, then Cory would never forgive Kristina for allowing it to happen. He was a restless sleeper and often he would talk, so softly that she couldn't hear a word he said. Occasionally, she heard a name, one of the girls — once or twice, her own name.

It doesn't mean a thing, she told herself. Cory's just not interested. He's built a life around his girls and he won't allow anyone else in.

When he did wake, it was instant. His eyes flashed open and he smiled at her.

'You still here?'

She got up and went to his bedside.

'How do you feel?

'I want to go home!' He pulled a face.

'Big baby!' She laughed. 'You can go home next week — if you're good.'

'All this power has gone to your head!' He laughed. 'Just wait until I'm better. Look, pass me those bags will you? I want to sort out the girls' presents before they come.'

Kristina helped him sort out dolls and souvenirs and sweets from all the different countries he'd visited.

'You didn't think I'd forget you, did you?' He smiled, handing her a box.

'Me?' She blushed. 'Oh, Cory, you shouldn't . . . '

'Open it now,' he urged. 'Before they arrive.'

Her hands shook as she opened the box.

'It's lovely.' She took out the vase with its collar of entwined hearts. 'Beautiful. Cory, thank you!'

'I did intend to bring you flowers, as well, but — the flowers will have to wait. You will get flowers, Kristina, I promise you.'

She dared to meet his eyes. He had such lovely eyes, so warm, so softly grey and the way they were looking at her . . .

'I wanted to bring you something romantic, but I'm not a very inspirational person. I'm good at my job, good with figures and languages and all the rest, but when it comes to really important things . . . I'm sorry, Kristina, you deserve better than this!'

'Cory!' She set the vase aside and took his hands in hers. 'I love it, really!'

'There's this, too.' He took out the perfume.

'Cory!' she exclaimed. 'This really is too generous.'

'What I'm trying to say,' he said, then shook his head. 'Kristina, I — you're more than just a friend to me. I know — I know you've lots of boyfriends and you probably wouldn't look twice at a widowed father of three, but — '

'Cory,' she said, tears washing over her smile. 'Cory, say it, say it!'

'I love you, Kristina!'

'Oh, Cory!' She hugged him. 'I never dared hope — I love you so much — '

They were both laughing as Kristina's tears stained both their faces. He kissed her, holding her tightly and she clung to him, never wanting to let go.

'I don't know how it took me so long to realise,' he said. 'It just struck me, like a bolt from the blue! I realised I wasn't just missing my girls — but you, too. And your visits to the house were the highspots of my week!'

'Oh, Cory, mine too — mine too!'

Then a voice broke through the laughter and the tears, a voice Kristina knew well — one she knew had the power to destroy their happiness.

'Shall we go out and come in again?'

It was Mark Jacobs. Kristina drew back from the bed, quickly mopping at her tears, but no-one noticed her as Cory's girls rushed in, surrounding him, smothering him with kisses and filling the room with their cries of joy.

This was where it would all fall apart, Kristina thought. Cory would learn of her disloyalty, her betrayal and the love it had taken him so long to discover, would be snuffed out as surely and quickly as a candle flame.

He would think that she had encouraged Mark Jacobs and blame her for the shattering of his happy family.

The bed was a mass of tissue paper and empty boxes as the girls opened their gifts. Kristina glanced at Mark. He was standing back with Paula at his side. They were holding hands and Kristina noticed how tense and anxious Paula looked in comparison to Mark, who seemed calm and laid back — a man who had made a decision and was happy with it.

Emma, too, seemed different. Perhaps it was seeing Cory looking so much better, but perhaps it had something to do with a decision of her own.

Cory had never looked happier or more content. He'd lost that shadow bereavement had cast in his eyes two years ago and his face was bright and youthful again. Kristina clenched her fists, knowing the shadow would return, perhaps never to be banished and she would have been instrumental in putting it there.

With Amy and Jodie engrossed with their new toys and Emma sitting on the bed beside Cory, Mark stepped forward.

'I realise this probably isn't the time or the place to bring this up,' he began gruffly. 'But I think it would be best if we cleared the air.'

'Mark, no, for pity's sake,' Paula pleaded. 'Can't it wait until he's at least out of hospital?'

Paula was a nurse. She'd know the detrimental effect bad news could have on Cory's health at this stage. Despite outward appearances, he still had a long way to go before he was back to full health.

Kristina flashed a look at Emma. She was sitting on the bed, holding Cory's hand, but she was looking at her birth father, Mark, with something close to adoration in her eyes. It was a look that, rather than touching Kristina's heart, struck it with a cold bolt of fear. There was so much at stake, so much to be lost, nothing to be gained.

'No, Emma and I have discussed this and we decided it was best to get it out in the open.'

Cory's face was ashen, his eyes ringed black with fatigue and worry. Had he been fully fit, Kristina had no doubt that he would have been on his feet and facing up to Mark Jacobs.

'Go on,' he whispered.

Kristina closed her eyes. She knew that whatever Emma's decision, Cory would abide by it — even if that decision broke his heart.

She moved closer to the bed, took Cory's other hand in hers and squeezed it. The look he gave her was one of unity, togetherness, she was a part of them now. Whatever they faced, they faced together.

'I asked Emma to come and live with us at the Smugglers. She's considered it now and I believe that she came to her decision without any pressure or outside influence being brought to bear — '

Paula snorted her disagreement, but said nothing, stilled by a look from Mark. Kristina could feel her heart thundering behind her ribs and knew that Cory's would be doing the same.

'The fact is, that Emma feels her place is with her dad. The man who has been father to her for as long as she can remember — '

Emma got up off the bed and went to Mark, putting her arms around him.

'She's also decided that there's room

in her life for me! Not that I deserve it, but there you are, we don't always get what we deserve in this life! However, I think we've reached an agreement which will suit all of us. Emma will have her own room at the inn which will be hers whatever happens, but her home will remain with Cory and her sisters, that's where she wants to be, where she belongs.'

'Oh, Mark!' Paula put her arms around Mark and included Emma in the embrace. 'I thought . . . Oh, never mind what I thought. This is wonderful news.'

Mark moved forward, offered his hand to Cory and Cory took it firmly in his grip. The two men smiled at each other, their eyes no longer hostile and suspicious, friends. Firm friends now with Emma to bind them.

The doubts, the fears, the frustrations all suddenly melted away and Kristina was left, a woman in love and a woman loved.

Cory still had all his girls — he

always would! And Mark had finally won the love of his daughter.

And it seemed, that at long last, Beatrice Versey was going to get her wish! And not before time, she might say and Kristina would wholeheartedly agree.

THE END

We do hope that you have enjoyed reading this large print book.

Did you know that all of our titles are available for purchase?

We publish a wide range of high quality large print books including:
Romances, Mysteries, Classics
General Fiction
Non Fiction and Westerns

Special interest titles available in large print are:
The Little Oxford Dictionary
Music Book, Song Book
Hymn Book, Service Book

Also available from us courtesy of Oxford University Press:
Young Readers' Dictionary
(large print edition)
Young Readers' Thesaurus
(large print edition)

For further information or a free brochure, please contact us at:
Ulverscroft Large Print Books Ltd.,
The Green, Bradgate Road, Anstey,
Leicester, LE7 7FU, England.
Tel: (00 44) **0116 236 4325**
Fax: (00 44) **0116 234 0205**

*Other titles in the
Linford Romance Library:*

WOMBAT CREEK

Noelene Jenkinson

Single mother Summer Dalton arrives
from New South Wales to her grand-
father's small farm in the Western
District. However, memories of her
hippy parents' banishment for their
free-loving morals — decades before
— remain. Her hope is to settle on
the land she's inherited, so she refuses
her new neighbour Ethan Bourke's
offer to buy her out. Then, a jealous
old flame and Ethan's disapproving
mother come into the mix. Can Summer
and Ethan resolve their growing attrac-
tion to one another?

CONFLICT OF HEARTS

Liz Fielding

Lizzie was astounded when her widowed father decided to marry Noah Jordan's beautiful sister. Thinking that now was the time to find a husband of her own — she wasn't about to accept Noah's marriage proposal . . . Noah was rich, gorgeous, charming, but to him marriage to Lizzie was a means of keeping her under control — a temporary measure to give the newly-weds time alone. But Lizzie, determined not to become a convenient bride, faced Noah — who was equally determined to have her!

MY SECRET LOVE

Margaret Mounsdon

When Tamara Cameron's modelling career is cut short after she suffers an injury to her back, she runs a private catering business, relieved to be out of the media spotlight at a time of personal difficulty. But then, scatty Phyllis Morton appears on her doorstep and Tamara's life begins to lurch from one crisis to another, as Phyllis turns out to be the great aunt of Adam Penrose — a man whose marriage proposal she turned down years ago.

KEEPING SECRETS

Della Galton

Twenty-two years ago, Joanna gave up her baby girl for adoption, but she has never forgotten her. When Caroline comes back into her life Joanna is both thrilled and afraid: her son, Robbie, doesn't know about Caroline's existence, and Joanna's marriage to Mike is in crisis. Her long lost daughter couldn't have arrived at a more turbulent moment. Only time will tell if Caroline's presence will reunite the family or destroy it altogether . . .